It is clearly in our interest to stop destroying and to start understanding our estuaries. They are vital places not only to the plants and animals that inhabit them. Estuaries in good working order are also essential to the proper functioning of earth's life support system as we know it. Which means, of course, that they are essential to the survival of man.

Edge of Life

The world of the estuary

by Peggy Wayburn

Photographs by Dennis Stock
With an introduction by Paul Brooks
Designed by Charles Curtis

A Landform Book
Sierra Club   San Francisco • New York

For my family—
immediate and universal.
P. W.

Produced in New York by Charles Curtis, Inc.

Film set in 11 point Trump by
Composing Room + Graphic Arts Typographers, Inc.,
New York.

Printed and bound in Italy by Mondadori
Editore, Verona. Library of Congress Catalogue
Card No. 76-189969. International Standard
Book No. ISBN 87156-057-7.

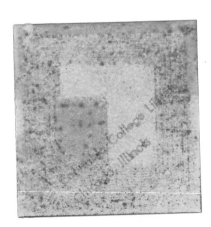

Introduction... 6
Prologue.. 8
Part I: The world of the estuary
1. The quiet pageant....................................... 12
2. The land form.. 18
3. The green world.. 32
4. The hidden world 46
5. The aerial world.. 58
Part II: The edge of life
6. The spiral and the star.................................. 80
7. Man in the estuary...................................... 90
Part III: The life and times of a West Coast estuary
8. Bolinas Lagoon...104
Envoi..128
Notes on ecology...130
References...139
Acknowledgments...144

Introduction

In his newly acquired dominance over nature, man will love and cherish only what he can understand. Among the well-documented prophecies of doom for life on earth as we have known it, amid the gathering darkness of murky skies, wounded land and poisoned water, there appears one ray of hope. For the first time in Western history, there exists a widespread, ever-growing knowledge of the natural world in its infinite variety and complexity; a recognition of the essential role played by each part in creating the living whole. This has not come about by chance. Within the last few decades, talented writers have been interpreting the laws of nature for the layman in virtually every area one can think of, in popular terms, on a scale hitherto unknown. Today in our dealings with natural systems as well as with each other, ignorance of the law is no defense; the facts and basic principles are there for anyone who can read. For example, we can no longer, as our forebears once did, consider as "wasteland" any swamp or marsh — or estuary — whose use to man was not obvious. While the word "ecology" has already been misused and vulgarized almost beyond recognition, the idea it stands for has become part of our common culture.

Romantic "appreciation of nature" is all very well. Indeed it is indispensable. Without the insights of the poets and philosophers of the past two centuries, we should be a lot worse off than we are. Without some saving sense of humility, some emotional response to forces beyond our understanding, we shall never succeed in turning the tide. Yet in the practical political world of self-styled "realists" we need practical weapons — answers, for example, to the question "What good is an estuary?" As Winston Churchill said at the outset of another battle for survival: "Facts are better than dreams."

From the point of view of both esthetics and utility, there is no natural environment more in need of creative interpretation. In the popular literature the estuary has been curiously neglected. Even the term itself has various definitions. Derived from the Latin word for "surge" or "tide," it is a place where, under certain conditions, salt and fresh water meet, creating uniquely favorable conditions for the propagation of life. As scenery, an estuary does not have the sharp impact of a snowclad mountain or a chiselled canyon; its beauty is more subtle than spectacular. And though there is always drama where the land confronts the sea, an estuary at first glance may seem tame compared to a deep blue fjord or crashing waves on a rockbound coast. The estuary's immense importance in the scheme of things is not immediately apparent. To appreciate it one has to live with it a while. That is precisely what Peggy Wayburn has done.

Though this is a book about estuaries as land forms, it is focused, quite properly, on one estuary—Bolinas Lagoon, north of San Francisco—which the author has studied over the years at every season and in every mood; whose beautiful surroundings, including a steep valley with herons and egrets that nest atop the redwoods and feed in the estuary itself, are as familiar to her as her own backyard, and whose mud, I dare say, will haunt her nostrils and cling to her boots for the rest of her life. This literal immersion in the subject is what gives her book its sense of intimacy. When she generalizes, she does so on the basis of first-hand experience. With nature as with nations: the initial step in understanding a people is to get to know one person really well.

Conservationist, hiker, plant lover, author, editor (including the new edition of *The Last Redwoods*), Peggy Wayburn prepared herself for writing this book through intense study and field work in ecology and marine biology. An "amateur" of estuaries in the root sense of the word, she has approached her subject with professional competence. Accurately but informally, she conveys a mass of fascinating information about this teeming cradle of life where so much of what goes on is hidden from the eye. Sensitive to the beauty of the estuary as a land form, aware of its unique position in the web of life, she knows that appreciation of both can come only with understanding. On this its survival depends. As Rachel Carson wrote in *The Edge of the Sea:* "Underlying the beauty of the spectacle there is meaning and significance. It is the elusiveness of that meaning that haunts us, that sends us again and again into the natural world where the key to the riddle is hidden. It sends us back to the edge of the sea, where the drama of life played its first scene on earth and perhaps even its prelude; where the forces of evolution are at work today, as they have been since the appearance of what we know as life; and where the spectacle of living creatures faced by the cosmic realities of their world is crystal clear."

Paul Brooks
Lincoln, Massachusetts
August, 1972

Prologue

The estuary is a fascinating land form, complex, dynamic, and full of magic. Maps rarely capture its character. A good atlas shows long narrow islands lying parallel to our southeast coast, for instance, but fails to hint of the vast marshlands and tidal flats that lie behind them. A small-scale map of Alaska hardly conveys the fact that two-thirds of its coastline is estuarine. And a road map picked up at a filling station suggests that there is no such thing as an estuary at all.

All this is not entirely the fault of the mapmaker, for an estuary is difficult to delineate. Its margins, as may be seen readily from the air, are likely to be curiously ill-defined. Unlike the clean-cut shore of sandy beaches outlined by a white curve of surf, its shoreline is more likely blurred. And the estuary may look entirely different at high tide and low tide; what appears in the morning to be a vast wetland of mud and marsh braided through with channels of shining water may be seen in the afternoon as a widespread shallow bay. This is because rivers (except in fjords) rarely enter the sea directly or tidily: they sprawl out over the land, scoop out bays, or butt against spits or barrier sand bars. And the sea is never still. The estuary, being the place where these two active land forms encounter one another, is itself in a state of never-ending change.

Such a place may be difficult, too, to explore on foot. Muds of tidal flats are often soupy, and it is disconcerting—to say the least—to step forward to see better the lift-off of shorebirds in a breathtaking spiral of flight and find oneself floundering knee-deep in muck. Hip boots are required footgear, and they are not always adequate.

Even on the higher ground of salt marshes the going can be rough. Except at the lowest tide there may be an inch or two of water covering the ground you walk across. Soggy holes are hidden in thick grasses. Channels with their odd-colored oozes—purple and orange or olive-green—have deceptively crumbling banks and are difficult to ford. One must get around little pools or salt pans, their bottoms fuzzed with algae that bubble slowly in the sun.

There may be other obstacles, too. Some marshes are covered with dense jungles of grasses, taller than a man. In the tropics, most swamps have impenetrable thickets of mangrove roots. Armies of small crabs or strange little snails may challenge the presence of one's feet on their territories. The water in the channels is dark and turbid, and there is sometimes rank gas in the air. (It is said that in ancient times Egyptians who owned estuarine land found it simple to evade taxes, for the assessors would not make their way around the marshes to determine the boundaries.)

From the vantage of a small slow-moving boat (preferably silent), however, one gets a different view of the estuary. Then the channels offer pathways from the ocean to the river and higher land. Around a bend may be herons, egrets, or roseate spoonbills, exquisite in flight. One may surprise a porpoise at play, or in certain parts of the world watch a white whale streak upchannel to feed when the tide is high. And in almost any estuary one feels in the quieter reaches the deep mysterious rhythm—the relentless elemental lift and drop—of the tide.

But not many people view the estuaries from small slow-moving silent boats. And fewer still don hip boots to explore them. Too often we approach our estuaries as the ancient Egyptian assessors did and, finding them difficult to travel, we avoid them. Then we turn to maps, or look down from a plane, or more recently, we form conclusions from what we see out a car window as we race across a seemingly monotonous swampland on a freeway built on fill.

It is small wonder, then, that we so often consider our estuaries useless, even unpleasant, places, "unfit for human habitation" and waiting to be put to some good use. On this assumption, we have diked and drained—and destroyed—a great many of our estuaries, "reclaiming" them for farmland or pastures or subdivisions. We have dredged countless others for harbors of various kinds, and rimmed their shores with concrete. We have also used them, whenever convenient, as cesspools for the cities that we have built around them, and we have piled our solid garbage high on the "wasteland" of their marshes.

And why not, one may well ask? Why not put the estuary to good human use as we do the rest of the earth? What is so special about this particular land form? Why should we leave it alone or give it particular care?

The answers pour out almost too fast. Because the estuary is one of the most naturally productive places on earth. Because it is a trap for solar energy as well as for nutrients essential to life. Because it is a place where these nutrients are put to work, employed by many life forms, exchanged and cycled. Because it is a spawning ground, a nursery, and a home, for numerous creatures of the sea. Because we, ourselves, depend upon many of these creatures for our food. Because it is a place where our water and the air we breathe are naturally cleansed. Because it has played a vital role in the evolution of many different forms of life. Because, indeed, life itself may first have sparked into being in the estuary and been nurtured there. The list goes on.

But it is not enough simply to list glib answers. We need a deeper understanding of the estuary, a land form so long overlooked or disregarded. That is the reason for this book.

Part I:
The world of the estuary

1. The quiet pageant

The estuary I know and love the best lies an hour's drive north of my home on the California coast. To reach it, I take a narrow winding road that does not hurry. Nor should it. For twenty miles or more it follows the shape of the land, curving around the green flanks of a mountain through fragrant stands of laurel, oak, and young redwood, and passing through meadows colored blue and orange with lupine and poppies in the spring. As I travel this road, some of the most beautiful vistas in the world spread out before me. There is a dark blue bay, a white city, an ocean seen often through a faint shine of fog. And then there is the estuary. Bolinas Lagoon.

I see it first from the mountain's high seaward ridge. It lies to the north, a small triangular wetland delineated on two sides by land, and on the third by a long sand spit, white-rimmed with breakers. On flood tides, it looks like a pale luminous lake with a bat-shaped island resting in it: at such a time it makes a mirror for the sky, for clouds, or for dark moving fog-shadows. Ebb tides bare its vast stretches of salt marshes, sandy shoals and mud flats, and weave a gleaming mesh of tidal channels among them.

The road to the estuary leads on down a long steep grade, around hairpin turns and through a small town. Then it runs beside the estuary's longest shore, tracing the toe of the mountain which meets the water here. Carved through the millennia by streams that rise on the high ridge above, the mountain is deeply indented by many canyons, each with a wet meadow and a culvert to carry its waters into the marsh. From this shore, the estuary appears as a broad band of water against the sand spit that makes a dark streak on the horizon.

Some three miles along, the road angles sharply toward the sea and travels along the base of a mesa. Eucalyptus trees form a high tunnel and spice the air with their fragrance. In fall, monarch butterflies come to hang by the thousands from their long slender leaves, being shaped and colored like leaves themselves when their wings are folded. Viewed through a trailing curtain of eucalyptus, the estuary now looks like a quiet blue pool, lapping against the tall mountain ridge that is softened by meadows and streaked with dark canyons.

Once more the road turns sharply, this time to cross the wide delta of a small river, and then the river itself, which flows beneath a green arch of alders and willows. The road goes on past a village with an old faintly New England air. One last turn, and it ends abruptly at the sea.

Westward the earth curves off into the endless ocean. Northward stand sandy cliffs pocked with the nests of kingfishers. To the east lies the estuary and the island. Southward churns the estuary's channel, the sand spit forming its other shore. I stand for a moment smelling the sea, feeling on my face a faint salty spray, listening to the wild cries of sea gulls. Then I put in my canoe and paddle into the estuary, for this is the best way to enter its world and encounter its beauty.

Consider the pageant unfolded when the tide swings here on a March day. Come at noon when the sun is warm. There is a lingering shimmer of fog fresh in the air. The tide is at flood and the estuary is brim-full, its glossy waters awash with the pale blue of the sky, its salt marshes all but drowned. Sea birds rest on its surface, a clutch of ruddy ducks, black brants, scaups and small sooty coots that upend themselves and disappear from sight at the slightest sound.

Close to the island's shore a great blue heron stands as motionless as a bent stick caught in the muddy sand, its elegant head tilted, its yellow eye intent on the shallows at its feet. Two egrets like white clouds float down, trailing their delicate nuptial plumage. With unexpected awkwardness they plunge their long black legs into the shallow water, then fold their wings and compose themselves, like the heron, into waiting statues reflected perfectly in the still water.

On the far side of the island, a pod of harbor seals lies sunning on the sand, the young within easy reach of their mothers. Their coarse fur glints in the sunlight, dark spotted gray and tawny brown. When startled, they flounder toward the water, undulating over the sand and making remarkable speed on their flippers. They plunge beneath the surface and then bob up their heads, one by one, to stare back curiously with round brown eyes at the intruder in their waters.

The world of the estuary moves to its own rhythm. Outside the barrier spit of sand the tide begins to turn and run out, but within the pulse is slower, the basin holds the waters, and the sea lingers at flood. There comes at last the moment when the tug of the moon becomes irresistible, and the sea begins its long retreat. The river and the canyons' streams, swollen with winter rain, have for six long hours been opposed by the pushing tides. Now they are quietly released. The estuary's waters drop slowly, almost imperceptibly, and narrow bars and flats and unsuspected islands emerge. The retreating sea forms a pattern of twining and intertwining channels. Through the narrow mouth of the estuary they join together and flow in a growing glass-green torrent.

In the new shallows fish leap and flash; the smooth black fins of a sting ray cut a sinuous parallel through the surface. The sea birds grow restless. As though to an unheard signal, they rise and separate out into bands of their own kind. The geese, with long outstretched necks, form a wedge that dips and sways, cleaving the pale sky as the birds point northward.

Where the blue heron and the egrets stand near the island, the water

13

The channels offer pathways from
the ocean to the river. Around a
bend may be herons, egrets, or
roseate spoonbills…And one feels
the deep mysterious rhythm of the
tide.

slips silently away. The blue heron begins to stalk, lifting each foot clear of the water and placing it stealthily ahead. When a fish comes too close, the big bird strikes with incredible speed. The heron dips the fish in the water, shakes it and turns it head first to gulp it down. Then the great bird stands immobile, once more like a crooked branch, its long neck distended as it swallows its prey.

The sunlight wanes, and the pull of the tide continues surely: the flats and bars and islands grow larger. Water remains in small pools on higher ground and on the island. In the orangey mud, crowds of snails in pointed armor make tortuous paths. Little crabs scuttle sideways along the edges of tidal channels, hiding themselves as best they can among the grasses.

There are now large stretches of wet muds and sands and marshland. At first glance they look empty, but they are full of life. The bottom-dwellers are hidden, having retreated downward in their tunnels as their world was exposed. If you listen you can hear soft clicks and smacks. And if you look closely, you can see small round holes with films of water pulsing to the movements of unseen creatures. A silver fountain spurts to mark the place a clam is lying. Another spray erupts and the blunt end of the clam's syphon probes a mat of green seaweed on the surface.

The shorebirds arrive unexpectedly. Like a shower of aspen leaves in the wind the peeps fly in from the south, wheeling against the sky, now vanishing as they turn away, now catching the slanting sunlight on their breasts. They move as one, swooping and turning again and again, the air humming to the beat of their wings. At last they settle on the mud flats with a long sighing sound. Folding their wings, they rest. Then each takes off on its quest for food, pushing its pointed bill into the muddy sands, peeping steadily, moving at random and leaving a delicate tracery of footprints. Willets crowd in with flashes of their showy chevron-striped wings. Long-billed curlews and godwits stalk on their stilted legs, thrusting their long slender beaks deep into the sands and muds. So softly colored are the shorebirds that they blend into the tans and brown and grays of the marsh.

Two terns with slender pointed wings arrive to fish a tidal channel. They cruise above the moving water in a straight purposeful path, pointing their orange beaks down, turning their heads from side to side as they scan the surface and the shallows. Spying a fish, one plummets unerringly to make the catch, then turns back to cruise the same course once again.

As the estuary continues to drain, the higher marshes become firm enough to step upon. Ponds dry out and cake beneath the late afternoon sun, their tenants now burrowed deep. Acres of muds and sands and grasses are spread wide to the coming twilight. Two boys with shovels on their shoulders and pails swinging in their hands walk out onto the flats. Soon they are finding clams. The only sounds are the thunk of their shovels and the cries of the sandpipers.

Time passes. Offshore, the tide again begins to turn, but the rhythm of the estuary holds and for a long hour its waters pour out in a strong flood. Still the changing sea persists, creeping up the outer beach and moving on inexorably until, soundlessly, the current changes and the basin once more begins to fill. Water seeps in slowly, drowning the sandy

There occur in this small estuary elemental processes — the capture and exchange of energy, the trapping and cycling of essential nutrients, the rich production of life support for myriad plants and animals.

flats and bars and islands, invading the marshes. The channels widen; the ponds and pools begin to disappear. The harbor seals move higher on the beach. The shorebirds feel the water on their feet and they, too, find their way to higher ground, resting among the marsh grasses.

Soon the bottom of the grass is wet, too, and the birds flock together more tightly. Then spiralling into the air like snowflakes whirling in a winter storm, they wing away and fade into the darkening sky. The terns are gone. The boys have come ashore, their buckets heavy with clams. The seals sleep. The scene fades into the soft lines of a brush painting. Venus is suddenly there in the west, blazing in the pale green evening sky. It is time to take the canoe from the water, for the pageant of quiet beauty appears to be over.

But it is not over, nor will it be. As long as the estuary remains, there will be a continuous procession of new events occurring: that is part of its magic. And much more is happening here in Bolinas Lagoon. There occur in this small estuary elemental processes common to all estuaries—the capture and exchange of energy, the trapping and cycling of essential nutrients, the rich production of life-support for myriad plants and animals. While other estuaries will be discussed in the pages that follow, this one—with its quiet pageant—will serve well as a model as we consider a complex, dynamic land form that is important to all of life.

2. The land form

On a cloudy late-summer afternoon, I stood on a mountaintop in the Far North. It was warm, and my boots were wet from the soft snow I had climbed across to gain this unfamiliar summit. Below me was the snowfield and I could see a small clear icy trickle of melting water being loosened from it. The freshet made a pleasant tinkle as its waters tumbled over the steep arctic meadow, through tundra starred with the white blooms of saxifrage and tapestried with the low leaves of crowberry and bearberry and blueberry, beginning now to bronze and burn gold with early fall color. The bright waters of that freshet, I thought, would travel ultimately and necessarily to a distant sea. I was witnessing in small part the genesis of a great Alaskan estuary.

In my mind, I followed those waters on their journey. As they plummeted downhill they would be joined by other alpine strands that drained the nearby slopes and ridges, so that when they reached the lower flanks of the mountain they would be part of a full-throated, fast-moving stream. Clear and shining as liquid glass, they would curve then between banks of low willow and alder and stiff plumes of fireweed, plunging finally through a mixed forest of spiky black spruce and aspen with pale straight luminous trunks and shimmering green-coin leaves.

At the foot of the mountain, this stream would meet another whose headwaters rose in distant mountains I could see, mountains painted orange and rust and chocolate brown. Still clear and sparkling, the waters of the two joined streams would pour over large chunks of rocks and churn into white foam before they met and merged with a milky glacial river that drained a huge massif of snow peaks on the far horizon, one of the great ranges of the continent. Moving fast and powerfully, they would mound up in the deep and narrow gorge ahead and then spread out in flat gray braids, twining and intertwining, pounding on at a hard relentless pace, rolling the stones of the broad river channel until they beat and ground against one another.

Lost in that wild turbid flow, the alpine waters would spill at length into the Yukon, the great river that drains the continent along a course of more than two thousand miles. They would travel then along a majestic pathway, swinging around huge loops and spirals, part of a massive smooth brown flow, swollen with the inpouring of other rivers along the way. Finally the melt-waters of the snowfield at my feet would meet the sea in a great estuarine system, a place of tides and mingling waters, of small rivulets and marshes, where white whales race upstream on the filling channels, a place of deltaic lakes where wild birds congregated by the hundreds of thousands.

On its long journey, I knew, the stream I was watching would loosen and carry particles of the earth over which it flowed, beginning with the rock beneath my feet. It was very ancient sediment, quarried from an earlier continent by a primeval river system and laid down eons ago as clay and sand on the bottom of a primitive estuary or the shallows of an old sea. Long since compressed and baked and crumpled by the restless earth, it had been upthrust finally in the hills of this range as shist, the oldest rock anywhere in the region. There were riches in it perhaps greater than the gold men found nearby half a century ago: there were minerals and nutrients necessary for the continuance of life. A scuff of pebbles from my boot onto the melting snow would start them on their return to the sea, on travels which might take centuries or untold millennia. Along the way they would be crushed, unbound and reduced once more to ultimate grains of earth.

Mixed with these particles, the river fed by the freshet at my feet would carry, too, a wealth of organic matter gathered by all the waters flowing into it. Bits of the leaves of berry bushes, the peat of tundra and muskeg, needles of spruce, the white bark of aspen, cells of plants and animals done with growing, of blades of grass and bone and sinew, all needed for new life, these elements would be washed into the veins of the great river system and carried into the distant estuary. There the sea would add its own rich burden and the alchemy of its waters and the energy of its tides. The estuary would churn and mix its waters, winnowing out essential nutrients, trapping them and holding them, making them available to plants and animals which would weave them back into the web of life.

As I stood reflecting on the extraordinary link between the mountaintop and the distant estuary, a warm rain began to fall gently and steadily. I pulled on my poncho and crouched beside a sheltering rock to wait out the shower, watching the raindrops spatter into the snow at my feet.

Soon I noticed that the waters spilling from the snowfield were beginning to swell and quicken, fed by the rain and freshly melted snow. If I were to consider the beginnings of the estuary, I realized, I would have to look further than the top of a mountain with its melting snowfield. I would have to look back into the elemental cycles and ultimate processes of the universe. I would have to consider the great outpour of energy from the sun, and the universal force of gravity which was not only bringing rain to wet my face, but was responsible for holding the planets in their courses. I would have to consider, too, how water moves, how air presses onto lakes and seas and rivers and gathers their moisture, forms it into clouds and storms, how mountains intercept storms, catching and channeling their rain and snow back into streams that move forever to the

Earth's rivers…form a huge,
constantly moving and changing
web over the land. Sculpturing
the earth, channeling their own
courses and rechanneling them at
will, they plunge, leap, carom or
meander lazily like live things.

sea. I would have to consider the ancient processes by which the earth thrusts up mountains, lifting the bottoms of seas into high peaks and then returning them again into the deeps, continuously moving the elements of sands and rocks and soils. I would have to consider how life ignites non-living matter, juggles atoms to nourish itself, takes the energy stored in a molecule of carbohydrate and uses it to breathe, to grow, to think, to love, to procreate. I would have to consider how living and non-living matter reacts and interacts to cycle and recycle so many of the elements necessary for life.

I would have to consider all these things and perhaps more, for the estuary was not a separate place with a beginning and an end. It formed an essential arc in many of earth's cycles, an essential link in many elemental processes. The place where the waters of the land and sea came together carrying their riches was a settling pool for the sediments of mountains and oceans and a storage place for the nutrients needed for life. Perhaps the site of life's genesis, it was now a place of constant renewal and regeneration of life, a part of life's ongoingness.

The rain was growing stronger and stirring with a cool wind. It was more than a passing late-summer shower, and so I left the summit of the mountain and made my way down, following beside the small musical stream, my feet slipping on the wet tundra. Along the way I stopped and put my hand in the tingling water, letting it slip over my fingers as it took its course to the sea. I pressed my hand against the ancient rock of the stream bed. There was green-gold moss growing on it, tough and firm and springy, born from the rock, I mused, requiring the stream, the estuary, the sea, and the storm. In the end, it would go to nourish new life itself. The genesis was unending.

What is an estuary? A land form without beginning or end, true. An integral part of earth's processes. A necessary segment in the arc of many great natural cycles. An environment essential to many forms of life. All true. But these things can be said of many land forms, and the estuary is unique, with characteristics unlike any other. It is a special place of its own. How to define it?

Because the estuary is complex and dynamic, it has inspired a spectrum of definitions. One of the broadest takes the tidal influence on inland waters as the criterion: it proposes that the estuarine zone is that "geographic zone...between the landward limit of tidal influence and the three-mile limit seaward." Since tidal influence often extends many miles up a river (as much as 600 miles up the Amazon, for instance) this would encompass a very wide strip of earth's coastal lands. Another broad definition uses the salinity of the water as the definitive index. One expert marine biologist insists that the edge of an estuary is bounded by the influence of earth's sweet river water on the ocean's brine. To him the whole of the North Pacific and much of the North Atlantic are properly estuarine areas, being freshened by streams and rivers and the meltwater of great ice caps. To him, the salmon and the shad, the smelt and the sturgeon—indeed all the anadromous and catadromous fish—are estuarine species. Between these two definitions, a good part of the planet might well be considered an "estuarine zone."

On the other hand, the definition of an estuary may be very narrow indeed. An oceanographer may consider it simply an arm of the sea that is modified by a river. A biologist may call it a region of a river that is influenced by the sea. And a geographer may describe it strictly in terms of the coastal land that it involves. Some biologists, too, insist that an estuary be differentiated sharply from other coastal land forms such as lagoons: they spell out certain limits of water depth, salinity, density, particle size of sediments, and shape.

Such narrow limits, however, are arbitrary. A common working definition says simply that the estuary is the place where the land's waters meet the waters of the sea. This covers almost everything from tideless inland seas to seeps along the shore that braid across wet sands and make a small alchemy in the waves. But since the word *estuary* comes from the Latin *aestus*, or tide, a more classic definition describes the estuary as the place where the land's waters encounter the sea under the aegis of the tide. Since the land's waters are generally gathered into channels or well defined waterways, we may say that a typical estuary has an inflowing stream or river which runs year-round. While not as grand a definition as the broadest given above, this is still broad enough to suggest that estuaries lie in many places along the earth's shores. As one biologist has noted, "estuaries... and their marsh and mud flat fillings constitute a much higher percentage of the world's coast than is generally recognized."

It becomes apparent immediately that estuaries must be both enormously varied and variable. Belonging to the river, the land, the sea and the shore, each will be as different as its component parts, and each of these parts is itself a dynamic land form. Add the further important dimension of the tides—which themselves differ in different parts of the world—and the complexity of the estuary becomes even more evident.

Consider the great variety of earth's rivers which flow into the sea. They form a huge, constantly moving and changing web over the land, each stream being a long attenuated edge or changing interface between fresh water and soil. Sculpturing the earth, channeling their own courses and rechanneling them at will, they plunge, leap, carom or meander lazily over the land like live things. In times of drought they may move listlessly; in times of flood, they form enormous conduits of raw energy. Always they are pulled inexorably by gravity toward the particular sea which finally claims them.

Rivers pluck continuously at the rocks and earth over which they flow, quarrying the grains of the continents and carrying them in their waters. Their waters consequently are as varied as the land beneath them. Rivers that rise in mountains of granite or other hard, tough rocks run clear and bright (or once did). Those that travel through areas of peat or muskeg may be tea-colored or even black with organic riches. Some rivers flow red with the mud they gather from the sediments of ancient coral seas which form their beds; some are brown with loam they loosen from unstable soils. Those which rise from glaciers begin as frozen streams that grind the land beneath them into fine floury particles, then melt into glacial milk.

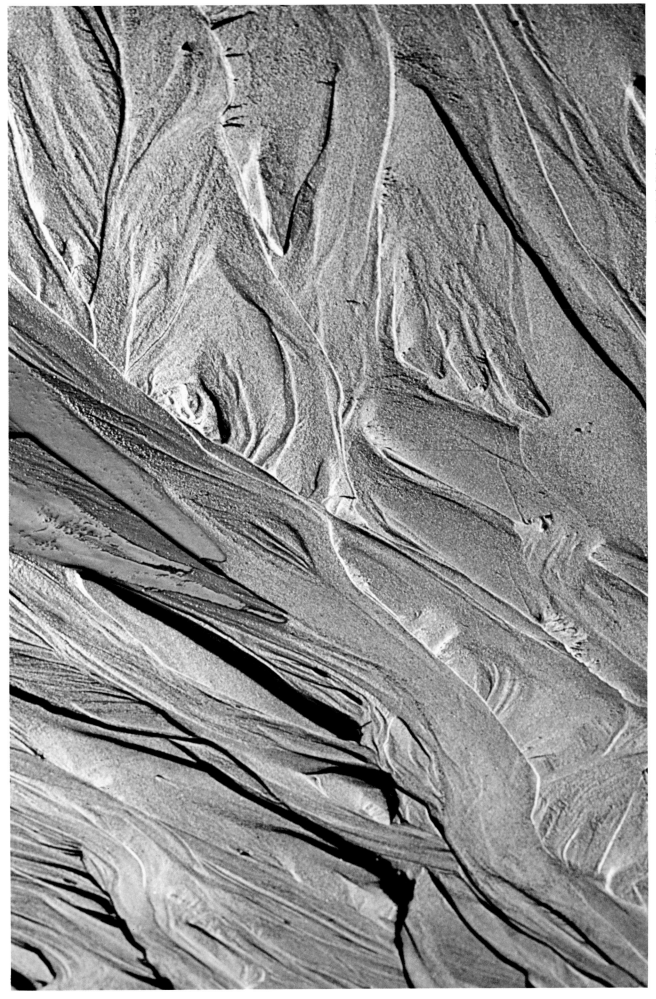

Some rivers flow red with the mud they gather from the sediments of ancient coral seas which form their beds; some are brown with loam they loosen from unstable soils.

The earth has many rivers, and names like the Yukon are the threads of man's history...the Tigris, the Tiber, the Ganges, the Volga, the Rhine, the Nile, the Amazon, the Thames, the Hudson, the Mississippi, the Columbia, the list rolls on. With their tributaries, they drain thousands of square miles of the earth's lands. Where they meet the sea, there are areas of enormous richness, and their influence reaches far offshore. And when a number of large rivers empty into the sea close to one another, they may produce grand estuarine zones indeed. In the Gulf of Mexico from Corpus Christi, Texas, to the tip of Florida, for example, there are between 15,000 and 20,000 square miles of estuarine waters.

Smaller, more modest rivers which drain only a watershed or two have a special charm and character of their own, as do their estuaries. There are many such along the west coast of North America which may be easily seen (although too often their mouths are bridged by freeways). Bolinas Lagoon is fed by several small streams that plunge headlong from a mountainside in winter storms, and by a small steady year-round river which drains about 5,000 acres, a comfortable area to wander through and to explore.

Every stream and river, of course, takes the easiest route to the sea, finding the nearest coast and shaping its estuary there. Coasts, being dynamic edges themselves and in a constant state of change, differ in character as much as rivers do. Estuaries are often considered or classified according to the kind of coastline wherein they are formed. Where the ocean has risen to flood a mountain range and a river pours out from a drowned canyon, the estuary is known as a fjord. Where an estuary lies on an earthquake fault, it is called tectonic. Where the coastal land is in fact the submerged shore of an ancient sea, rivers and shallow offshore waters together may build up sand barriers or bars parallel to the shore; these help contain the so-called bar-built estuaries, and there are classic examples of these lying all along the eastern and southeast coasts of North America. Many estuaries, too, are drowned river valleys, Chesapeake Bay being a prime example. In fact, this complex estuary includes many river systems which have been inundated by the rise of the sea in recent geological times. There are also deltaic estuarine areas formed by rivers that carry a heavy load of silt, like the Ganges, the Yukon, and the Nile. While deltas as such tend to smother active estuaries and create lakes and lagoons, new, albeit short-lived, estuaries form constantly where the river water enters the sea.

Not only do coasts differ greatly, but so do regions immediately offshore; and these areas, too, influence the estuaries. Along the east coast of North America, for instance, the continental shelf slopes gradually into the Atlantic Ocean and there is a wide band of shallow water; the force of the sea is widely dispersed against the land. On the west coast of the continent, however, the continental shelf drops off close to shore, and the land rears up abruptly from the deep water. The direction of the Pacific Ocean winds and the effect of the earth's motion, the Coriolus Force, cause the upper layer of the water to move seaward, allowing colder water carrying rich nutrients to upwell close to the shore. Wave action is strong and concentrated, and acts as a major force that continuously erodes the land. Along the coast of Alaska, the continental shelf is generally wide. In places such as the Bering Strait, shallows extend for hundreds of miles offshore; in other places, however, steep rocky cliffs lift out of the water to form fjords of un-equalled beauty.

As the river and the land work together to shape an estuary, the sea with its currents and tides adds its own unique influence, and it too is different in differing parts of the earth. While all the oceans ultimately come together to form one continuous body of water, each has its own individual character. Its currents are powered by solar radiation, and, carrying heat or cold, swing as the planet swings in space, determining the temperature of the water and modifying the climate of the land around it. And the tides give each sea its own particular rhythm.

Tides have a kind of magic about them. Hitched to the movement of heavenly bodies, they are one of our visible links to the universe. They change as the moon changes, as it travels around the earth in its elliptical journey. When the moon is closest to earth, at perigee, it exerts its greatest pull. Then a full round moon pushes up over the horizon, or a new moon cuts the evening sky with a thin sharp scimitar, drawing the waters high on the land in spring tides. When the moon is most distant, at apogee, its force is weakest and the seas slosh around, moved only slightly by neap tides.

The sun, too, pulls on earth's waters (and lands as well). When the three heavenly bodies—earth, moon and sun—are aligned, celestial forces peak: tides are at their strongest, running at full flood when high, baring the secrets of the sea's coastal floors when they ebb. When the moon is at apogee and the sun hangs at right angles to it, earth's waters are at their quietest.

Tidal changes vary all over the world. In some places, such as the Gulf of Mexico, there is only one tide a day; in others there may be two tides a day, but they will not necessarily be equal as they are along the Atlantic coast. On the Pacific coast the semidiurnal tides vary in their strength. Tidal range, too, varies greatly, depending upon the configuration of the land. Along most of the eastern seaboard the range is generally small, yet in the long narrow inlet of the Bay of Fundy, which lies between Maine, New Brunswick, and Nova Scotia, there are great racing tides with a range of up to forty feet. The west coast has a turbulent line of scrimmage between the sea and the land in many places. At Cook Inlet, Alaska, the sea ebbs a half-mile offshore, and then rushes in at speeds as great as nine miles an hour, producing some of the world's highest tides. The daily tidal range may be thirty-six feet on spring tides.

Having distinct barriers against the sea—bars, islands, or sandspits—many estuaries, especially those with narrow bay mouths, tend to hold back their waters against an ebbing tide. They establish their own tidal rhythms which may lag considerably behind those of the open shore. In Bolinas Lagoon, for instance, there is a tidal lag of about an hour.

Winds may work along with the tides and add a major force to an estuarine system. Blowing onshore, they may reinforce a tide on flood and spread it out into a broad prairie of water, flattening its waves like grasses in a strong gale. Blowing offshore in a heavy storm, they can offset tidal action and, at ebb tide, may help drain an estuary's basin of its sea water. Before the Zuyder Zee was "reclaimed" for dry land, the circulation pattern of this great estuarine region—the common delta of the Rhine, the Meuse, and the Scheldt—was greatly affected by the wind, which is still described as coming off the North Sea "like an ax... cleaving (a person) to the bone." The Zuyder Zee, incidentally, was one of the world's greatest fisheries—before it was filled.

Oceans carry a burden of sand, however variable, in their waters, and rivers always bear a load, however large or small, of silt. The basins of estuaries form settling pools for these sediments. This accounts for the vast areas of marshland that build up along estuarine coasts. It also explains why estuaries eventually fill up, sometimes slowly, but inevitably, to become drier and drier marshland and finally, meadowland. Like lakes, they are ephemeral land forms, each having a more or less brief life expectancy measured in geological time. Like all shores, too, they are subject to submersion when the sea rises, or to uplift when the land itself moves. Like mountains, they are very ancient land forms: there have been estuaries since there has been land to catch rainwater and channel it to the sea. They have formed and filled and formed again, and they will persist as long as there are seas and rivers and shores, if man will allow them to.

Considering their complexity and variability, it is no wonder that estuaries differ so much in individual shape, size and character, and that they are called by so many different names. There are sloughs and waddens, bays and sounds and inlets, bayous and firths and fjords, gulfs, deltas, lagoons, bights, harbors, saltings and esteros, capes and straits and channels —all may be estuaries.

By whatever name, estuaries and their adjacent uplands have been attractive places for human habitation since earliest times. Now they are the sites of most of the world's great cities and metropolitan areas—New York, Boston, Washington, Tokyo, Osaka, London, Shanghai, and Buenos Aires, to name a few. Between 80 and 90 per cent of the Atlantic seaboard and the Gulf of Mexico is a nearly contiguous estuarine zone, one of the earth's greatest, most heavily populated, and varied.

Along the North Atlantic, the glaciated shore is rugged and often deeply incised with inlets. The sea water is cool and rich with nutrients. From the New York bight southward, great coastal plain estuaries rim the continent and the land is lapped by warmer waters from the Gulf Stream. In the Gulf of Mexico, the Mississippi River pours out the drainage of the mid-continent to mix with sediments quarried from other states by such rivers as the Rio Grande, the Brazos, and the Chattahoochee. This coast is swampy in many places, with lush bayous. The west coast is less obviously estuarine, although there is run-off of fresh water in the rainy season, of course, along all the shoreline. And San Francisco Bay is one of the world's most magnificent estuaries, a classic example of the tectonic land form.

From Washington's Puget Sound northward there stretch other estuarine areas of incomparable richness. The shoreline of Alaska runs 33,000 miles from its southern boundary, where it is brushed by the cool waters of the Pacific, to its northeast terminus, where it is most often locked in the ice of the Arctic Ocean. In between there are 22,000 miles of estuaries of all kinds and shapes and forms—from the tectonic Lynn Canal to the fjords of the southeast to the estuarine coastal plain Arctic Slope to the magnificent deltas of the Copper River, the Yukon, the Kuskokwim and the

There are sloughs and waddens,
bays and sounds and inlets,
bayous and firths and fjords,
gulfs, deltas, lagoons, bights,
harbors, saltings and esteros,
capes and straits and channels—
all may be estuaries.

Colville. The meltwaters of some of the great remaining icefields on earth freshen hundreds of miles of this coast, which comprises nearly half the estuarine zone of the United States. This priceless treasure supports some of the world's most productive fisheries.

It seems curious that estuaries, which form such a significant part of the landscape, have gone so long unnoticed, unremarked, unstudied, and unsung. Not until this century has their real significance been recognized, and then only slowly. Even now, there is no branch of science devoted wholly to them as there is, for instance, to lakes. There is no such thing as an "estuarologist" or an "estuarian." Instead scientists from many disciplines— microbiologists, hydrologists, physicists, chemists, geographers, among others—consider the estuary from their own special points of view. As a result, the literature on estuaries tends to be fragmented, many different opinions are voiced, and much remains to be studied and understood. The total role of the estuary in the ecosphere has still to be defined. Some of its physical workings have, however, been explored: how the irresistible force of the river meets the irresistible force of the sea, for example, and what happens to the energy contained in both.

Without tides, the river's water theoretically would flow unchecked onto the ocean. Being lighter than sea water the fresh water would presumably float on top of the surface of the brine for great distances before the two waters would finally melt into one another, mixed by the interfacial friction between them. This happens to a degree where there is a large outpour of fresh water that enters the ocean through a narrow channel, as in a fjord or other deepwater estuary. There the river loses contact completely with its bed soon after it encounters the sea. The heavier sea water forms a wedge along the bottom and the band of fresh water flows over it, sometimes for quite a way offshore. A saltwater wedge and the banding of fresh water and brine are thus considered by many to be classic indicators of a true estuary.

At the interface of fresh and salt water, however, other reactions may occur: river water, especially if it is flowing swiftly, tends to create its own waves along the surface of the sea water. At the same time, the raw energy of the tides pushes the salt water upward. The gravitational and tidal forces in the two waters collide. They spend their energy in churning and thoroughly mixing the river water and the salt water and their contents. As a result, oxygen in the fresh water—considerably greater than that in salt water—is distributed throughout the estuary, and wastes are carried off.

Along with the thorough mixing of earth's waters, another "edge" phenomenon takes place in the estuary, a kind of fringe benefit. There is an alchemy when fresh water and salt water encounter one another: the sediments they carry are affected in curious but predictable ways. Fresh water transports its sediments largely separated out in suspension. Its particles of rocks, soils and clay (clay particles are so fine they are submicroscopic in size) travel downstream like infinitesimal kites borne on a strong wind. When they reach the estuary, the force carrying them is fragmented; the heavier particles, which may be thousands of diameters larger than the smaller clay particles, tend to sink, and the tidal action sorts them out according to their size. The tiny particles, however, react to the salts in sea

If the estuary was indeed the cradle for life…if it was the land form that nourished the first feeble flicker until it grew strong and burned bravely, life has reciprocated in full measure.

water by pulling together: they flocculate (a nice word that comes from the Latin, *floccus,* meaning tuft of wool) and form loose fluffy masses of suspended matter. Since they are buoyant (the smaller the particle, the higher the ratio of its body surface to its weight, the easier it floats), they are easily winnowed by tidal currents and many are swept into the quieter parts of the estuary where they take their time in settling out during tidal lags and neap tides when the waters are calm. Here they form beds of clay.

And so both the tides and the alchemy of the estuarine waters sort out the silts and sediments that wash in from the river and from the sea. They account for the pure sand bars found near the mouths of estuaries, for the beds of sandy muds and muddy sands that form salt marshes, and for the beds of clays. The latter have singular properties of their own which add to the extraordinary character of the estuary.

Because their molecular structure is such that they are charged negatively, clay particles have an attraction for many other molecules and the atoms of some elements. In fresh water, they may pick up calcium, or bond with oxygen and hydrogen, hanging on to tiny droplets of fresh water and storing them even when they settle out in the estuary. In the brackish water and the brine of estuaries, they attract many other elements, including potassium, carbon and nitrogen. Layered in sheets on the floors of the estuary, clay particles form lattices over which the tides may wash every known element, for they are all found in sea water. Trapping the organic particles —the carbon, oxygen, phosphate and nitrogen, the stuff of stars and the stuff of life—the clays help line up amino acids, basic building blocks for new life. It may be that in the estuary's shallows the delicate edge between inorganic and organic matter is crossed continually. This is one reason it is argued that the estuary may have been the site of the genesis of life.

The estuary, then, is a sort of magic pool, the site of many fundamental natural processes, an efficient "nutrient trap," as biologists call it. But being designed to catch, hold and accumulate many elements, the estuary also traps poisons. Its clay deposits have an affinity for heavy metals as well as for the organic riches. In San Francisco Bay, for instance, a measurable input of mercury has been washed down the Sacramento and San Joaquin Rivers for many years. Mercury carried naturally from the cinnabar deposits upstream has been augmented since the 1849 Gold Rush days by mercury used to separate gold. It is estimated that 120,000 or more pounds of mercury now lie embedded in the floor of the Bay. While not harmful to man in its natural form, mercury is lethal when microorganisms work it over and change it into methyl mercury, one of its organic compound forms. The micro-organisms have had decades to work over the deposits in the Bay. If the bottom is now disturbed—dredged, as is proposed, to deepen it—no one can project just what the effects will be or how much of this deadly poison will be stirred up and released to be incorporated into the aquatic food chain.

Aside from having remarkable physical properties, alchemy that gathers elements and concentrates them, and a mixing process which circulates them, the estuary performs many other functions which are invaluable to people. The water of most estuaries (fjords excepted) is shallow: at mean high tide, for instance, most of San Francisco Bay is less than fifteen feet deep. Shallow water tends to break into many small waves rather than a few large ones when it is stirred by winds or even light breezes. Small waves roll the air on their surface through the water, absorbing its impurities, forming an efficient filter system which in effect scrubs the air and re-oxygenizes water. Buoyant river water on the surface provides more oxygen for exchange than salt water does. Mud flats, too, add a major input of oxygen into the air: they soak up molecules of H_2O when wetted by high tides, and release the oxygen through evaporation when the tide ebbs. In areas of heavy smog, therefore, estuaries may play an important role in refreshing the air people breathe. "Reclamation" and filling of estuaries cuts down, of course, on this valuable process. It may also affect the climate, since a given body of water absorbs more heat than a comparable body of land. A bay makes for a far more pleasant and livable climate than an area of "reclaimed" land. Such reclamation not only destroys the vital earth processes of an estuary, but it can raise the temperature measurably.

Estuaries also provide valuable open space, described by biologist Rene Dubos as a "biological necessity" of human beings. In a crowded metropolitan area such as that which so often surrounds a bay or harbor, the water itself may provide the major open space resource.

Estuaries which lie along coasts frequently battered by cyclonic storms serve still another purpose: they break the fury of such storms. Their offshore bars act as breakwaters, absorbing the major impact of heavy waves, while their basins take the initial flood of sea water and hold it from the land. The wave action of shallow water, described above, also breaks down the force of heavy winds, in effect draining their energy.

The esthetic value of a great estuary can be immeasurable, as anyone who chooses to live on a sparkling bay will know. The charm of more intimate bayous and saltings and open salt marshes (the latter described so lyrically by the poet, Sidney Lanier) has enchanted many people, too.

Invaluable land forms, estuaries, even without the plant and animal life they support. But they cannot be considered without this life, for their life-giving qualities are their most important gift of all. Plants and animals—some submicroscopic in size—cram themselves into every possible part of the estuary to take advantage of its richness. Some use the place for a nursery, some for a shelter, some for a permanent home. Partaking of its ready-made hospitality, they contribute in return great riches of their own. Not only do they feed themselves, but often produce or provide extra food to support countless other populations that live on the land, in the nearby sea, and in the air. In their life processes, too, many estuarine dwellers also concentrate, cycle and recycle essential elements and make them available to other life forms. If the estuary was indeed the cradle for life—as it is often said—if it was the land form that nourished the first feeble flicker until it grew strong and burned bravely, life has reciprocated in full measure.

In every part of the ecosphere, in every ecosystem, the earth and the life it supports are inseparable, being linked inextricably. In the estuary as perhaps nowhere else, however, so bountiful is the environment and so prodigious is the total life it supports that the whole is greater than the sum of its parts. Life joins with this place of magic to make it one of the most productive environments on earth.

31

3. The green world

It was mid-morning of a day in early June, and the Georgia sun already poured out a flood of tangible heat. It pressed on my face and bare arms like a hot scarf, and I could see it form a trembling band against the distant horizon where the sky, a deep soft blue above, was light yellow and sultry. I sat in the bow of our small boat watching the prow cleave the dark, opaque water, admiring the way my companion was guiding us through the estuary. The tide was dead low, and it was impossible to judge the depth of the channel.

We moved through a forest of grass. When I stood and looked about I could see it stretching endlessly in every direction. As tall as I, and taller, the cordgrass crowded to the very edge of the channel, its sturdy stalks thrust deep into the wet marsh, its long pointed leaves forming a continuous canopy. The effect was strange; it was a world of monotony, of hot sky arched overhead, of pure stands of lush grass going on infinitely, of green water slipping beneath us, of the soft throbbing of our motor. It reminded me inevitably of traveling through a wheat field in eastern Washington. There the whole bowl of the sky was bright blue and the air was snapping clear and cool the day I passed through. The wheat lay like an endless golden carpet on the gently rolling fields, and we drove easily on a straight and well-paved road. Still, the feeling was the same: the salt marsh with its grasses was like a floating wheat field.

The analogy might even be broadened. At the University of Georgia, classic studies have been made comparing the wheat field to the salt marsh and its grasses in terms of productivity and efficiency. Both were considered as monocultures, the one man-made, the other natural. The index of comparison was the dry weight of organic matter grown per acre in the wheat field and in a salt marsh of a Georgia estuary not far from where I traveled that hot June day. The wheat field came off a poor second. It produced only one and a half tons of foodstuff (counting stems and leaves as well as seeds) to the salt marsh's ten tons. And not only was it less productive but far less efficient.

I considered the implications of these studies as we followed the pathway of the channel toward the sea. The wheat field is a manufactured land form, I thought, and therefore demands an enormous input of manpower and machine-power just to get it going. The land must be cleared, plowed and weeded to produce a single crop. In many places it must be irrigated and almost certainly fertilized. Being a single crop—an artificial monoculture—wheat is particularly vulnerable to attack by "pests" and therefore requires the application of pesticides. The "pests" gradually build up immunities to the pesticides and new ones must be developed, or else new strains of more resistant wheat must be discovered. All this requires continuous and costly research.

Once ripe, the wheat must be harvested, winnowed, and packed up before it is shipped elsewhere as a raw product. Then another series of energy-consuming procedures follow before it ends up as flour or in loaves of bread to feed one species, man. And then the whole process of clearing, seeding and weeding must start over again. As far as I know, the total amount of energy required to produce a ton of wheat—let alone its subsequent loaves of bread—has not been measured, nor compared to the total amount of energy it will provide, but it might make an interesting study.

In contrast, the estuary is a natural land form, and its plants have evolved to fit into a rigorous environment. Cordgrass is especially sturdy. It grows with its roots submerged for long periods of time, and so it has an almost constant water supply. The plant reproduces itself abundantly, either through seeds or, more commonly, by budding from its underground stems or rhizomes; and in Georgia marshes it grows two crops a year.

The estuary supplies it liberally with natural fertilizer, nutrients carried in by the sea, the river, and those provided by other estuarine life forms. The tide, moreover, circulates the fertilizer and distributes it over the salt marsh, washing it actively around the growing plants; it also carries away waste materials. If the pure stands of cordgrass appear to be a monoculture, it is not because they were introduced and commanded to grow here: the plant has succeeded in the marsh and crowded out its competitors. While subject to the predation of certain insects, grasshoppers and beetles and such smaller creatures as thrips, it can generally resist them without too much damage to itself, using its own saltiness in place of pesticides. Different species of cordgrass have also hybridized themselves naturally and colonized new areas with great success.

Cordgrass provides food directly for insects (in fairness, so does wheat) and for birds with its seeds. In decomposition, it supplies food for myriad creatures of the marsh, the estuary, and—of enormous importance—the ocean. It is estimated, for example, that Georgia estuaries nourish at least two thirds of the local commercial fish and shellfish during one or more important periods of their lives. And the beautiful thing about it all is that the estuary and its salt marshes work by themselves, if simply let alone.

The trouble was, I thought to myself as I watched the orange-red fiddler crabs backing away among the forest of cordgrass stalks—the trouble was that you could not see what the estuary was doing. Its marvelous processes were taking place invisibly and going unnoticed. The estuarine system was simply too subtle. The crops it produced were not brought to table, like

33

lettuce or potatoes or apples. They filled no bins or tall silos. The "waves of grain" I traveled through were only endless stretches of grasses with glittering bits of salt crystal on their leaves.

So how, I wondered, could I describe the enormous richness of the life I knew—and sensed—was in this place? How tell of the wealth these rustling grasses held, wealth that would go to feed the invisible millions of organisms that form the broad base of the sea's great pyramid of life? How best portray the role that detritus, a word unfamiliar and faintly unpleasant, plays? How, in our bright, open world, explain a system of life where organic matter, decomposed in wet dark places, is the great source of food?

I watched the salt marsh recede behind us as the channel broadened and grew deeper. Our boat gained speed, cutting a wide white-fringed wake. Ahead of us lay a long sandy island, barring the estuary from the sea. Nearby a sleek dolphin curved in and out of the water, describing a black arc. A snowy egret stood motionless beside the island, small, exquisite, aloof, with golden eyes and delicate black legs. I watched the bird advance one foot cautiously through the water to stir up a fish or two. Then it stood motionless again to see what it had raised. We cut our motor and drifted toward the landing.

As I climbed ashore, I could hear the sound of the distant sea, the steady beat of the waves. Where I stood the dark water was lifting as the tide changed. A splash of liquid sunlight floated on it.

I recalled Sidney Lanier, the poet of the marshes, who wrote of another place not far away:

> Ye marshes, how candid and simple and nothing—
> withholding and free
> Ye publish yourselves to the sky and offer
> yourselves to the sea:
> Tolerant plains, that suffer the sea and the
> rains and the sun...

There, I thought, was the place to begin. To explain the living world of the estuary, I would start with the sun. With the sun, and with the green plants that alone have the secret of turning its energy into food.

Now, as it always has, all of life depends ultimately upon the sun. The rich wetlands of estuaries, spread wide open to the skies, are natural traps for solar energy. Concentrating the elements required for photosynthesis, and in prodigious quantity, they also have a wide variety of places where life can fit itself. They offer many niches in their sands and muds and clays, in their bars and flats and channels, along their shores, and in their changing, moving waters.

But with all their potential for life, estuaries also have stringent requirements for life to meet. Life must be able to tolerate the rigors of tidal change. It must survive the dessicating outpour of heat and light when low tides drain the flats and marshes. It must accept the shock of cold water when the sea changes, and it must endure long periods of submersion when the tide floods. There are problems, too, of variable salinity of the water, of shifting substrates, and of direct exposure to harsh winds and rains.

As I climbed ashore, I could hear the sound of the distant sea, the steady beat of the waves. Where I stood the dark water was lifting as the tide changed. A splash of liquid sunlight floated on it.

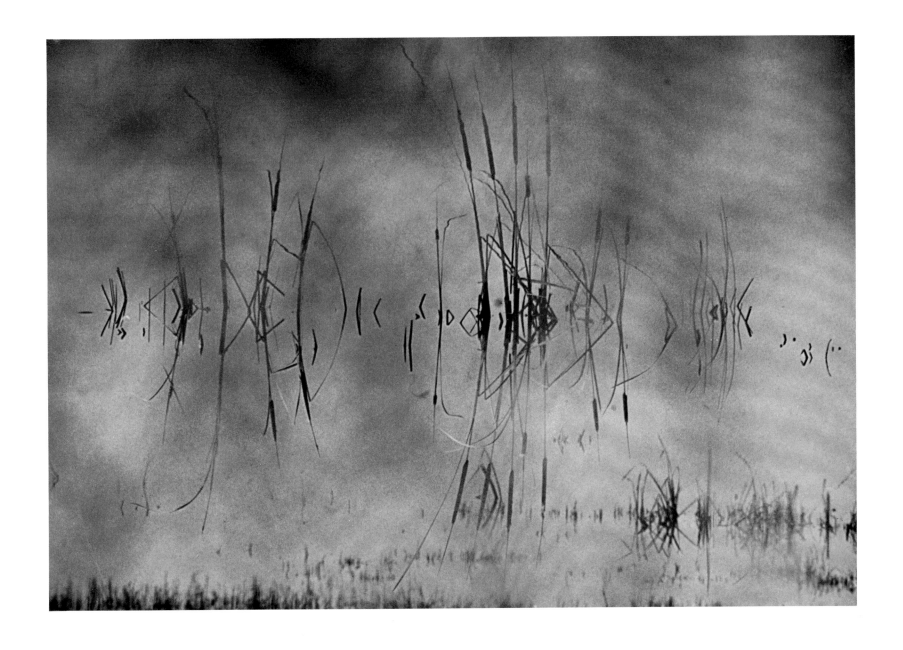

Under such circumstances, it is not surprising that many of the plants that crowd into estuaries are simple, primitive, resilient species. It is, in fact, conjectured that some of these plants, perhaps the earliest blue-green algae, evolved in the quieter, more protected regions of estuaries where the tidal action was gentlest. Managing to meet the demands of that environment, they were then set to develop through the eons into the great variety of algae which now populate every corner of the earth.

Today's estuaries provide homes to innumerable algae of all shapes and sizes, the greatest numbers of them—teeming billions of them—being microscopic. Some float in from the sea, some drift down the river; others live their entire lives in the estuary, occupying the muds, sands, clays, and all the waters from the river's inlet to the sea's salty channel. They may cling to rocks, marsh grasses, old pilings, or even live on larger species of algae, the big greens that thrive in estuaries, or the reds and browns that wash in from offshore.

The blue-green algae are the most primitive, the simplest of the green plants. Their cells contain the bare essentials for plant life—protoplasm and pigments. The pigments come in many colors—red, orange, gold, and, of course, blue-green.

Most of these algae are colonial, living close to one another, on one another, or in congregations which may make them visible without a microscope. Sometimes they appear as bits of blue-green jelly in sheets or strands or filaments along the banks of tidal channels or streams; sometimes they are no more than a tinge of color on the mud.

These lowly plants perform many valuable tasks. After trapping the sun's energy and converting it into edible sugars and proteins, they become a food supply themselves for numerous different forms of life. Certain estuarine blue-greens provide another essential service: they are among the only life forms that convert the nitrogen gas of our air into nitrates, which are required by all living cells. These primitive plants thus contribute significantly to the great nitrogen cycle, one of earth's elemental life-supporting processes.

Along with the blue-greens, other microscopic plants thrive in the estuary. There are the more sophisticated green algae, and the diatoms. Each time I find a diatom in the microscope I come up short, surprised anew by its exquisite form. Diatoms live inside of glass cases built from silica and etched in myriad fanciful patterns and geometric designs. Inside these cases are the plant's minute organs, each with its special function. Among them are chromoplasts, often arranged in discs of chlorophyll, stacked to form tiny batteries the sunlight will charge with energy. In terms of human life, diatoms live only briefly, surviving a day or two at most. They reproduce abundantly, however, and given auspicious conditions, they can replicate themselves ad infinitum.

Floating and drifting in the upper half inch of the sunlit water of estuaries are many planktonic diatoms which maintain their buoyancy by secreting droplets of oil inside their glassy cells. In the fall, a plankton net in Bolinas Lagoon will strain out hundreds of these plants, including many different species. Some, such as *Coscinodiscus,* float around as individual plants. *Coscinodiscus* looks like a miniature green-gold pill box with a

The estuarine system was too subtle. The crops it produced were not brought to table. They filled no bins or tall silos. The "waves of grain" I traveled through were only endless stretches of grasses.

highly ornamented lid. Other species are colonial and hitch themselves together in a variety of curious ways. Some have long thin spines with which they grasp one another to form chains. Some are concave at each end and fit together to make spirals. The individuals of one species stack themselves like microscopic pancakes, then stretch out to form an attenuated line, somewhat in the manner of a slide rule. This enables them to travel around at a great rate, contracting and expanding like a single organism. There are also diatoms that arrange themselves in circlets, their oval bodies barely touching one another, their long fine spines forming an elegant radial design.

In addition to planktonic species, many estuarine diatoms are sessile, or sitting, plants. These require a surface to live on or in. They may be equipped with miniature stalks to hang onto rocks or cordgrass. Or they may live on the bottom of the marsh's pools or salt pans, or in or on the clays, muds and sands. In fact, they occur in most estuaries in such profusion that they often create sheets of color on the tidal flats. They come in many hues, in olive-green and golden-brown, orange, and sable. Among them is *Isthmia* which traps, concentrates, and puts into the food chain vitamin B_{12}—one of the amino-acids required for healthy life.

Diatoms, like all life forms, have their own mysterious body rhythms, or biological clocks. Those that float in the estuary's deeper waters, like those in the open sea, stay near the surface as long as there is light. At night, they sink to the bottom and divide themselves into new plants. The benthic diatoms that live in the upper regions of the sands and muds of tidal flats have different time clocks. They need both sun and water, but not too much of either. They are programmed to move up and down in the sand to take advantage of optimum tidal and seasonal conditions. Certain species in cool climates inch down into the wet mud on high tides. When the water is low they inch back up into the sunlit shallows. Interesting laboratory experiments show that this phenomenon is not related to tidal action or the presence or absence of sunlight: in still waters and constant artificial light, these tiny plants continue for days to go up and down in their muds in perfect synchronization with the absent tides.

The algae in estuarine muds and sands provide food for many creeping creatures as well as benthic dwellers. At the same time, in their own life processes they produce oxygen steadily throughout all the hours of light. Those that float in the waters, both in estuaries and offshore, not only form the basic food supply for all marine life, but contribute oxygen to the air we breathe.

All algae have the ability to gather in and concentrate essential nutrients and other substances which may be in the environment around them. Unfortunately, they have no way of selecting against certain poisons which man has introduced into the ecosphere. Diatoms, for instance, can concentrate DDT at a phenomenal rate—increasing their content of this biocide by thousands of units in a matter of seconds. This starts a biological magnification that will continue up the marine food chain. The top predators, of course, whether fish, bird, or man, will get the heaviest dose of all.

Living closely with the diatoms in estuaries are the dinoflagellates. They are distinguished by two whiplike tails, one of which encircles the tiny

All these green plants of the estuary…grow in balance with one another, having worked out an equitable subdivision of desirable living space. And while the estuary appears idle…it is continuously producing a bumper crop of food.

body, the other of which propels the one-celled plant (or animal, depending upon the biologist describing it) vigorously through the water. Along with the diatoms, they are an immensely important source of food for marine life in estuaries and other wet places.

Certain species can bioluminesce—they light themselves up like microscopic fireflies. Washing into an estuary, gleaming green-gold like drowned moonlight, they outline the streak of a fish, the shape of a wave, the course of a canoe paddle or the path of a hand trailed through the water.

Other larger algae are common in estuaries, particularly the big greens, *Ulva, Cladaphora* and *Enteromorpha.* Certain species of *Ulva* are called sea lettuce since they are about the size of a lettuce leaf and have much the same color. The plant's thallus—or body—is as delicate as tissue paper, being only two cells thick. Stacked in sheets, *Ulva* provides home and shelter for many smaller plants and animals. *Cladaphora* is an inconspicuous branching green plant. Along with *Enteromorpha*—which looks like a tangle of bright yellow-green strings and often attaches itself to the shells of limpets—it provides an important food source for animals of the estuary as it breaks down in decay. The same is true of the brown algae, the huge ropy kelps that occasionally wash into estuaries from the ocean, along with the leafy boas, and the more delicately fringed red algae.

Other of the more primitive plants are found on higher and drier ground. Mosses and many lichens embroider marshlands with their subtle colors. Bracken, the most ubiquitous of ferns, may grow even in sandy soils. And larger fungi occur in the meadowy parts of the marsh.

The flowering plants are more recent in evolutionary time, more complex, sophisticated and demanding. The estuary poses a special challenge to them. Not only are there problems of sustained submersion, extremes of temperature, and brackish water, but the estuarine environment is hostile to most seeds. To take advantage of this demanding habitat, certain flowering plants have made major adjustments. *Salicornia,* for example, a dominant plant in many marshes, requires brackish water, and its seeds are programmed to sprout well in it. The beautiful eelgrass, *Zostera marina,* has equipped itself to live totally submerged for long periods even in brine. *Spartina*—the ubiquitous cordgrass that thrives from Maine to Brazil and from China to England (and worldwide in deserts as well)—has adapted to the most difficult place of all. It lives in the salt marsh's lowest tidal zone. Availing itself of the riches of this interface between land and water, it has become one of the most productive flowering plants on earth.

Consider some of the problems that cordgrass overcame in adapting to this place in the salt marsh. Land plants routinely need oxygen for their roots, but cordgrass has a particular need for plenty of this life-giving gas. Its body chemistry demands an unusually large amount of iron, which it must take from the soil by changing the iron sulfide present there into ferrous iron. This delicate chemical operation, performed by the roots, requires extra oxygen. The soil of estuaries is almost always anaerobic or completely lacking in oxygen, the supply having been used up by the billions of microscopic and submicroscopic plants and animals that inhabit the surface sands and muds. Cordgrass has therefore developed a system of small pipes that lead from openings in its leaves into its hollow stem, which forms a

Other life forms await the bounty
of food being prepared for them
and brought to them by the tides.
In this dark and unseen world
and on the salt marshes live some
of the most beautiful and curious
of all the creatures on earth.

conduit underground to big air chambers among the roots. Thus cordgrass supplies its roots with plenty of oxygen from the air. Since the whole plant may be underwater periodically, the small openings in the leaves close when the tide floods. If they did not close, the grass would drown.

Cordgrass has solved further problems just as neatly. Having evolved as a freshwater plant living on land, it must now tolerate brackish water and brine for long periods of time. To accomplish this, the grass has developed a filter device in its roots, which strains a maximum amount of fresh water into the plant to maintain healthy cells, and just enough salts to enable those cells to withstand the heavier pressure of sea water. Special glands excrete the excess salts, the sodium and chloride which accumulate in cells uselessly. These salts form the crystals that glitter on the grass like diamonds in the sun. Cordgrass has also developed a biological clock that enables it to survive for hours inundated by the tides. A west coast species, *Spartina foliosa*, for example, can tolerate inundation for twenty-one hours.

Being fed, watered, and tended by the tides, and having no competition, cordgrass can spend almost all its time and energy growing. Where most land plants can utilize only about one percent—or less—of the sun's energy that reaches them, cordgrass can use more than six percent, which adds enormously to its overall productivity as well as its oxygen output. Concentrating nutrients and minerals in such abundant supply in the estuary, making more food than it can possibly use itself, it stores its extra bounty in its leaves. Moreover, recent studies indicate that *Spartina* may also be able to absorb in its cells certain of the more lethal gasses that are found in smog.

Along the eastern seaboard, cordgrass was once used as salt hay for cattle, but today few animals feed directly on its leaves and stems except for a few insects and certain fungi. Cordgrass nevertheless provides nourishment to countless animals in a more subtle way.

Plants of the salt marsh grow in distinct zones. Cordgrass is the indicator plant—indeed, the only flowering plant—of the lowest tidal zone. In Bolinas Lagoon, thick stands of *Spartina foliosa* thrive on the island, in certain places along the shore, and on the delta of the small river. A shorter grass than its Georgia cousin, *S. alterniflora*, *S. foliosa* nonetheless looks for all the world like a typical monoculture. A strong green throughout most of the year, it turns a golden wheat-like color in the autumn.

Just above the *Spartina* grows the index plant of the middle zone of the salt march, *Salicornia*. This low-growing succulent goes by a number of common names. The annual species make delicious pickles, as the eastern colonists discovered—hence, pickleweed. The annuals are also good in salads, being crisp and salty, and so may be called saltwort. Because its fat stems have a translucent look, *Salicornia* is also referred to as glasswort. One species common in the east is shaped something like the foot of a bird and is called chickentoe. *S. virginica* in Bolinas Lagoon has the perennial's woody stem. In fall, it turns beautiful shades of orange and rose, crimson, brown and soft green, covering the marsh with a colorful tapestry.

Among the pickleweed's remarkable endowments is its ability to colonize salt marshes. Because its seeds and seedlings can tolerate salty water and survive in it for long periods of time, the plant may float around at

Now, as it always has, all of life depends ultimately upon the sun. The rich wetlands of estuaries, spread wide open to the skies, are natural traps for solar energy. They offer many niches in their sands and muds and clays.

various stages of its growth until it finds a place to take root —on a carpet of decaying algae, or a high mound of sand. Soon it establishes a small islet in the estuary. This pioneer plant literally lifts the land.

Like *Spartina, Salicornia* provides the habitat for insects and fungi as well as for scuttling shore crabs and certain snails and limpets that inch their way between the stems searching for diatoms. A stand of *Salicornia* also makes a good feeding and loafing place for shore birds. In the fall, I have walked out into the *Salicornia* marsh at Bolinas (usually wetting my feet in the process, for there is often an inch or two of water standing where it grows) and flushed a hundred or more willets, which opened their striking black and white wings against the luminous sky and yelled their annoyance at my intrusion.

An intriguing flowering plant, dodder (*Cuscuta salina*) is often found on *Salicornia.* It is a semi-parasite, and its bright orange threadlike stems entwine the host and send in tentacles to tap the nourishing sap inside. In spring, the dodder produces tiny white blossoms, and, later, seeds which can take root on the salt marsh. Some *Salicornia* marshes are colored orange with infestations of dodder.

The indicator plant of the marsh's upper zone is another grass, *Distichlis spicata* a ubiquitous saltgrass with short spiky leaves which, like *Spartina,* grows worldwide. This grass has also adapted to long periods of immersion in salt water and has glands to excrete extra salt; its leaves, too, may glitter with salt crystals. Its rhizomes or underground runners trace patterns on the upper marsh and help to anchor shifting sands.

Where the island in Bolinas Lagoon most closely resembles the coastal strand, a few conifers grow. The cones of pine and cypress provide seeds for certain birds and for the bright-eyed voles which tunnel through the *Festuca rubra,* a reddish bunchgrass tufting the sands in large stands here.

All these green plants of the estuary, from the tiniest of the algae in the sand and waters to the pure stands of cordgrass on the marsh, grow in balance with one another, having worked out an equitable subdivision of this highly desirable living space. And while the estuary, rising and falling serenely with the tides, appears idle indeed, it is continuously producing a bumper crop of food. The single-celled plants are for the most part consumed directly, along with some of the more complex algae. The larger algae and the flowering plants, including *Spartina,* are consumed as detritus —the decomposed bits and pieces of the plants' leaves and stems, and other decaying organic matter. Detritus feeds innumerable animals of the sea and land and air. Ultimately it feeds man himself in the flesh of shellfish, bony fish and wild fowl.

The idea of eating pieces of dead and decaying plants (and animals) is repugnant to most people. Yet we do it habitually, slicing up fruits and vegetables and cooking them until they decompose, and relishing "aged" meats. We are, in fact, like all living animals, efficient agents of decay and decomposition as we digest our food and return it to simpler organic form. Yet bacteria and microscopic fungi are more efficient decomposers —and they are infinitely more numerous. They comprise a large segment of the estuary's plant community. (Bacteria, it should be noted, occupy an anomalous place among earth's life forms, being classified as "protists," neither plants nor animals.) In the estuary, they perform the vital service of converting the leaves, stems and bodies of plants into pieces of detritus of edible size, chopping up the vegetables, if you prefer. Some pieces are snapped up when they are quite large, others get broken down further and further until they turn the estuary's water into a rich vegetable soup. The bacteria and fungi, of course, are often eaten right along with the organic matter *they* are eating. In fact, they form an immensely important food supply themselves for microscopic life forms as well as such filter feeders as clams and mussels

Sometimes a purplish film can be seen just under the top layer of tidal muds. This may be a colony of a curious species of bacteria found in estuaries. These purple bacteria are photosynthetic, demanding sunshine, but they cannot tolerate oxygen, and die when exposed to air. They perform the task of converting hydrogen sulfate into sulfur, which is used by other life. In the process they expel odoriferous gas, hydrogen sulfide, which causes some finicky people to avoid the marshes of estuaries and to think of them generally as unpleasant places. When ignited, this gas burns with an eerie blue glow—the Will O' the Wisp of many legends.

Drifting or swimming with the estuary's submicroscopic plants, tucked into every crevice and cranny, fastened into its muddy and sandy floors in a whole array of strangely contrived homes, other life forms await the bounty of food being prepared for them and brought to them by the tides. In this dark and unseen world and on the salt marshes live some of the most beautiful and curious of all the creatures on earth, the estuary's family of animals.

4. The hidden world

It is a cold, dark morning. Clouds over the estuary sag low, heavy with a burden of unshed rain. They look solid, like gray streaked stone, until they meet the mountain where they dissolve into thick mist. The top of the mountain is hidden. The lower forests are somber blue against the fields of faded autumn grass.

A strong surf pours onto the shore, pounding against the sand, laying down more sand to make a new berm on the beach, and bludgeoning the base of the cliffs to the north. The water is lead-gray, veined everywhere with white froth, and the waves come roaring in, unravelling long frayed streamers of spray. The rhythm of breaking waves is lost in a tumult of sound.

The wind is gusting in hard from the southwest, a sure sign of a good storm. It carries a scud of sea water that bites against my face. A few gulls sail above me where I stand on the island, their flight patterns gone awry: the wind skews them every which way and they tilt and dip and wheel to stay aloft. Their underbodies are white, and make a strange and graceful pattern against the dark sky. I can see no good reason for the birds to be there unless they share the sense of expectancy I feel, the long moment of wonder that seems to come before such happenings as dawn, or nightfall, or a storm like this one. It is the first big winter storm of the season, and late in arriving.

The wind grows stronger, and the gusts steady out, making a new high sound above the noise of the sea. The grasses on the island are laid flat; the pine trees and the cypress, usually stiff, almost formal trees, wave their branches with a kind of crazy, helpless abandon. I look up to see what the gulls are doing but they are gone. The island, I am sure, is empty of its shore birds, which move into the brush and meadows at times like this. I wonder briefly about the mice and voles that snuggle down among the roots of the grasses or go underground during most storms. Almost surely this land will be drenched with the flood of waves and rain that is coming.

For one last moment, I brace myself against the wind and let it pour over me, feeling the first stiff sting of rain. Then I make my way across the sandy strand to my boat, glad it's a Boston Whaler with a sturdy engine to get across even this short stretch of channel. The water is already racing, heaving with the deep rhythm pushed into it from the sea. The boat slaps hard against the waves. The landing float is slippery with rain, and riding the waves like a boat itself.

I climb ashore in a heavy gust of rain. Swags of limber eucalyptus stand out straight in the wind, drop back, stand out again, a few snapping and skidding across the wet, black pavement of the road. Leaves soar through the air. Everything living moves, each twig, each needle of the conifers, each leaf and petal and blade of grass. The wind and rain seem alive, too, and the world is drowned in their sound.

I had forgotten how marvelous a good hard storm could be, how cleansing of the land and all its life. The earth gets hosed down with sweet fresh water. Every plant and tree gets a grooming, each branch is combed clean of dead leaves and needles. When the storm is over, the ground, well-soaked and refreshed, will have a good layer of compost on it to nourish new life.

And what a feast for the creatures of the estuary, all the unseen life tucked into the muds and sands and waters. The grasses of the salt marsh will be stripped, their leaves carried into the water along with the bounty of the land borne in by the freshened streams. There will be a surfeit of food.

Wet to the skin now, I turn to push my way along the edge of the estuary, through the small town and up the hill to the house where a warm fire awaits me. It is the first real harvest of the year, I think, truly a time of Thanksgiving, although the fourth Thursday of November has already come and gone.

With productive plants adding their bounty to an already rich habitat, the estuary offers an unparalleled opportunity for animal life to flourish. At the same time, in all but its quieter reaches, it has limiting factors even more stringent for resident animals than for plants. The creatures must adapt to a constantly changing world. They must accommodate to alternate drowning and dessication. They must put up with widely fluctuating temperatures, hot sun and chilly sea water. They must accept the changing saltiness of the water as well as the shifting of the sands and muds of the substrate. And the sunlight, so welcomed by the plants, is often unnecessary—even harmful—to animals that live in wet places.

As testament to life's infinite inventiveness, a number of animals can meet these demanding conditions and thrive. Although somewhat limited in species, the estuary's permanent residents occur in great quantities. Along with them, many transient visitors exploit the estuary's richness, swelling the total population until the place teems with animal life. Creatures occupy every nook and cranny—the muds and sands, every level of the water, and the marsh lands as well. They also live in and on the plants and one another.

Not surprisingly, most of the full-time residents are tough and simple creatures from the more primitive ranks of life. There are swarms of microscopic protozoans in the waters. Numerous invertebrates inhabit the sands and muds. These soft-bodied creatures often build tubes or burrows for their homes, or they have shells or crustaceous cases to protect themselves. Many are marine forms which can tolerate brackish water as well as pure brine, but a few, like the oysters, actually prefer less salinity.

The richest places in the estuary are the edges or interfaces. The surface and bottom waters are crowded with life, and space is at a great premium. Competition among the zooplankton, or floating animals, is intense. Many of the tiniest animals are fierce predators, eating other microscopic animals including members of their own species. Competition among the benthic, or bottom, dwellers is greatest when the animals are mobile. Once ensconced in a tube or burrow, however, a creature may stay put peacefully for the rest of its life.

Consider the advantages of such a life style in the estuary. There is little problem of wave shock, and animals tucked away in tubes or burrows are relatively safe from attack. The tides tend them much as they do the plants. The moving waters carry food—detritus formed from *Spartina* and other marsh flora, numerous edible diatoms, and larvae and protozoans —to the waiting creatures, and wash away their wastes. Most benthic dwellers are filter feeders. Some have tentacles to trap detritus. Some spin mucous nets to seine their food. Some simply gulp down the mud around them and ingest the edible material, then discard the inedible waste.

Now the disadvantages. Since benthic animals take their oxygen from the water around them, their biggest problem is to avoid drying out. Tube-dwelling worms may employ their heads as stoppers to keep water inside their tubes during ebb tides. Snails seal off the entrance to their shells with a special secretion. Mussels and barnacles snap their shells tightly shut when the tide changes, retaining moisture inside. One interesting worm meets the problem another way: it has evolved a special crystalline hemoglobin which retains oxygen in its blood for several hours even when its burrow is drained dry.

Extremes of heat and cold can be almost as lethal as dessication. Since the greatest changes in temperature take place in the upper three or four inches of the tidal flats, many burrowers and tube dwellers make their homes deep enough to shrink into when the sunlight pours down. Several species are blind, having no need for eyes. Most, however, have eye spots or pigmented areas which react to light and shade. The feather duster worm, for example, is so sensitively equipped that the passing shadow of a cloud may send it deep into its tube. This lovely, fast-moving annelid is one of the most tantalizing subjects a photographer can encounter. The shadow of a foot being placed on the nearby shore ends all chances for a picture.

The mobile animals of the estuary avoid many of the problems of their more stationary neighbors. They simply swim into deeper places when the tide changes. To do this, they need to see. The bony fishes, being higher vertebrates, have long since evolved good eyes. Many invertebrates which move around—such as crabs and shrimp—have eyes even in their larval stages. The scallop has many bright eyes tucked between the halves of its shell; it swims, albeit jerkily, by clapping together its shell and pumping water out of its siphons.

The consistency of the estuary's substrate determines where the bottom dwellers live. Slimy muds or areas where sands are constantly scoured and shifted by the tides provide poor habitats. Where firmer sands and muds remain relatively stable, large populations crowd together. Certain species such as bamboo worms are choosy; they colonize an area exclusively, forming a sort of animal monoculture. Others, like the echiuroid worm, or fat innkeeper, and the ghost shrimp, dig their burrows next to one another and live as neighbors. Virtually none of the benthic animals resides alone. Inside of nearly every tube and burrow there are smaller symbiotic species living with the tenant.

The estuary's benthic dwellers perform important functions. They concentrate many of the free nutrients and minerals in the detritus they eat. Most of the burrowers are fastidious and remove their wastes from their homes as soon as possible, depositing it outside in small fecal pellets. Bacteria work these over and soon make essential elements available for reuse. Many mollusks are particularly important cyclers. Clams and mussels sort over their food carefully and separate out the phosphate, excreting it in pseudo-feces, so that it can be readily recycled. The little animals that spin their nets of mucous to trap food also capture clay particles and add them to the estuary's supply. The burrowing creatures play a further role: they loosen and open up the bottom soils much as earthworms do the land, allowing the water to sweep in oxygen and other vital elements.

The bony fishes that swim in from the sea also bring essential elements and excrete them in the estuarine waters. Many fish become stranded on tidal flats when the water draws down, and die, thus providing important nutrients for other forms of life. The anadromous fish carry nutrients further inland, using the estuary as a layover stop. Every creature has a special role to play, a niche to fill. Working together, they weave important threads in the web of life.

The best way to consider the estuary's unseen world, I think, is to use imagination. A microscopic view is helpful, and a haul of the plankton net makes a good point of departure to explore some of the estuary's strangely beautiful inhabitants.

In Bolinas Lagoon, the plankton net nearly always brings in a few protozoans and larvae along with the exquisite diatoms that float in these waters. The tiny animals are equally exquisite, and more varied. They are ingeniously equipped to live successful and useful lives. I often wonder about the concept of relegating them to the "lower" forms of life. In a single cell, they can perform all the functions necessary for life. They can nourish themselves, reproduce, and take advantage of circumstances that higher forms would find too trying. And perhaps most marvelous of all, they have within their protoplasm the same determination to survive, the same will to live and to perpetuate their species that the highest and most complex creatures have. In one tiny cell, they embody the prodigious wonder of life.

Consider the remarkable foraminifera—often called forams—of which there are several at Bolinas. These protozoa have shells that are often spiralled and designed as elegantly as the shells of tropical mollusks, yet it takes a high-powered microscope to see them. Forams come in enormous variety; more than 15,000 species have been described, and many more may remain to be identified. They help to capture and concentrate the calcium washed down by rivers and carried in the run-off of rain from the land. They are found in all of earth's waters. Forams are also important geological indicators. From fossil forams, oil geologists can fix the date of sedimentary deposits and the conditions—whether freshwater, estuarine or marine—under which they were formed.

In almost every plankton haul there will be a *Favella,* a tintinnid fringed with cilia or tiny hairs. This little animal secretes a glassy house often shaped like a wine glass. Fastening its body to the inside of the stem by a tiny elastic stalk, it can shrink down to the bottom to hide, or rise up to the rim to feed on diatoms and tidbits of detritus.

The larvae in the plankton net are apt to appear bizarre, and sometimes deceptive. They may look like a miniature caricature of the creature they will become, or they may give no hint whatsoever of the shape they will later assume. Thus, both worms and mollusks produce similar trochophore larvae having tiny globular bodies with tufts of cilia at either pole and a belt of cilia around their middles. A trochophore may grow into a long thin worm or a short fat clam. This seems to indicate that both clams and worms share a distant common ancestor. The larvae of crustaceans are just as curious. They recapitulate the various stages of the animal's evolution. The crab, for example, assumes five different forms as it matures. Each form resembles a different species from which the creature evolved—a different step in its evolutionary history.

If luck is with us, our plankton haul in Bolinas will hold an adult copepod or amphipod. These are more complex, many-celled creatures and are frequently large enough to be visible to the naked eye. The copepods that live in surface waters are among the most important of all the estuary's zooplankton. They are often the principal link between the plant and animal life, being voracious and highly successful primary consumers as well as predators. Amphipods, which may live tucked away between sheets of green algae, are an important food for many shorebirds.

Sometimes the tiny medusa of a hydroid is caught in our net. Hydroids are coelenterates, among the first in the evolutionary ranks to have both an outer skin (ectoderm) and an inner skin (endoderm). They assume two different forms during their lives. At one point they are colonial and sedentary. They then form buds that break off and float away to become jellyfishes, or transparent bell-shaped medusas, with a circlet of tiny tentacles. The medusa produces gametes, or sex cells, which unite to grow into another sedentary colony.

Although tiny worms such as parasitic nematodes and the perfectly transparent arrow worms may turn up in a Bolinas plankton haul, most of the worms in the lagoon are larger forms. The majority live in tubes, but a few like the brightly colored nemerteans—or ribbon worms—are free-swimming. Alone among all the members of the animal kingdom, the ribbon worm has a highly specialized eversible proboscis, a delicate sort of tentacle that can be stretched as long and thin as a fine whip, snapped out and coiled around the worm's prey. Ribbon worms are highly elastic. A three-inch worm can expand into an eighteen-inch animal and then retract itself to the original length. And its proboscis may extend as far again as its body, or further. Some ribbon worms fracture themselves into pieces when caught—and each piece has the ability to regenerate into a new worm.

Ribbon worms like to burrow around in the bottoms of estuaries where they may encounter—and seize for prey—an annelid worm, which is likely to be stationary. Annelids build many kinds of tubes, using mucous-cemented sand and mud and bits of shell. They may eat plankton, gathering it in when the tides are low, or they may feed on detritus and bacteria.

In Bolinas Lagoon, the feather duster worm, *Eudistilia vancouveri,* builds itself a deep tube with a frayed-looking collar projecting above the surface of the sandy substrate it prefers. It pokes out its head to feed on plankton. Its head is crowned with a plume of feathery gills resembling a carnation. The first time I saw one I thought it was a flower dropped into the water.

When the Bolinas mud flats are bared at low tide, there appear to be plantings of tiny brown twigs—hundreds of them—about an inch-and-a-half high. These are the tubes of the bamboo worm, *Axiothella rubricincta,* another annelid. Bamboo worms are jointed and garnet-red in color. Living with many of them is a tiny commensal pea crab called *Pinnaxa longipes.* In order to fit itself into the worm's narrow tube, the crab has evolved a body about three times as wide as it is long. To get into the tube along with the worm is tricky. The crab must first insert one claw and then slowly ease itself in after it.

In sandier places nearby—and best observed when tides are at their lowest—are colonies of *Phoronis viridis.* These small estuarine worms encase themselves in underground tubes which resemble miniature rolls of sandpaper. Each worm sticks its head out of its tube's opening and waves its plume of fuzzy green tentacles, feeling the water for food. Seen under an inch or so of water, the colony looks like a polka-dotted rug. The polka-dots may vanish before the watcher's eyes, however, for the worms shrink into their tubes promptly at the first sign of danger.

Low tides in Bolinas Lagoon reveal other curious scenes. The naked tidal flats resemble a lunar landscape of small volcanoes. These piles of mud with holes on top shelter several kinds of invertebrates, both worms and crustaceans.

Among the most intriguing worms is the aforementioned fat innkeeper, *Urechis caupo.* Commonly about ten inches long and an inch in diameter, this worm has neither eyes nor ears. It uses a short sensitive proboscis to nuzzle around in the mud until it finds a place to build its home. There it makes a burrow by pushing into the mud and expanding the girth of its body. The burrow is a U-shaped, hose-type dwelling having two entrances some thirty inches apart. Thus one fat innkeeper accounts for two

The naked tidal flats resemble a
lunar landscape of small
volcanoes. These piles of mud
with holes on top shelter several
kinds of invertebrates, both
worms and crustaceans.

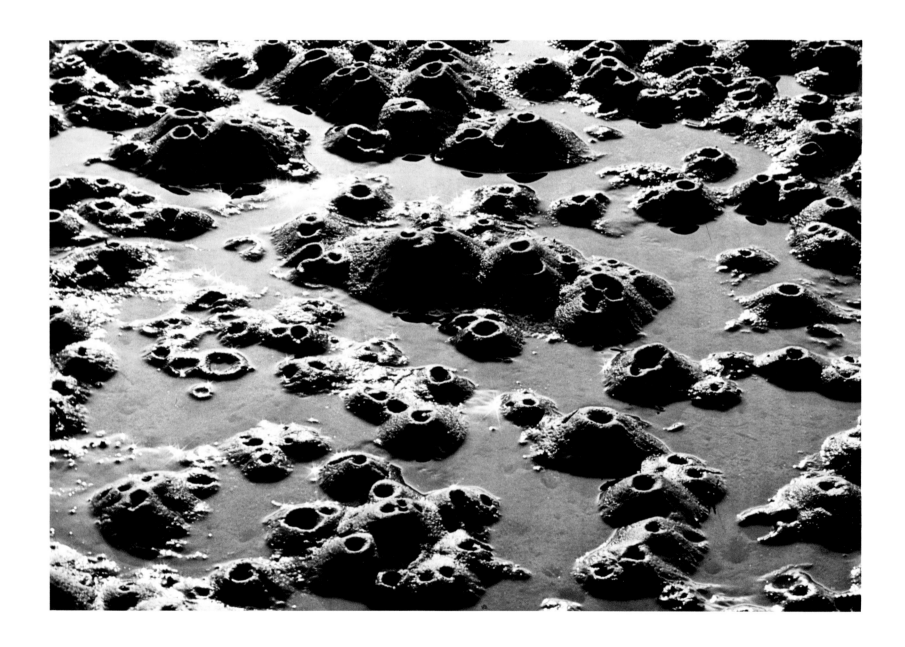

mud volcanoes. Once inside its burrow, the worm never leaves again. With the notable exception of the rays, which can get the worm out by using their broad flippers like suction pumps, few predators can reach the fat innkeeper. Its chances for a long life—up to twenty-five years— are therefore good.

Although sedentary, the fat innkeeper moves constantly in a series of rhythmic contractions that keep the water running through its burrow. It feeds by spinning off a tube of mucous with openings about 4/25,000,000 of an inch. One end of the tube is attached to a hole of the burrow. The other end is around the worm's neck. Still spinning away, it backs off, pumping hard with its body to force a strong current of water through the mucous seine. When it has collected a sizable catch of detritus and microorganisms, the worm detaches the net from the burrow and swallows it whole. But being a selective eater, it retains only the smaller morsels for itself and discards the rest for the guests that use its burrow for an inn — a pea crab, a larger scale worm, a goby fish and an inch-sized clam.

Living next door to the fat innkeeper in the Bolinas tidal flats are two species of ghost shrimp. The pink ghost shrimp is smaller, and prefers higher, sandier ground. It is a compulsive digger, tunneling out a complicated, never-ending burrow. When it stops digging, which it does rarely, it cleans itself rigorously with bristly appendages. One biologist describes it as being obsessed by the Puritan Work Ethic. The blue ghost shrimp lives a more relaxed life, grubbing in the mud, and straining out food particles with a basket made from two pairs of specialized claws. Both kinds of ghost shrimp live in pairs. The couples apparently stay together for what may be a considerable lifetime — as much as fifteen years.

Inside the burrows of these shrimp can be found some of the same commensals which enjoy the hospitality of the fat innkeeper: a clam, a scale worm, a small fish and a pea crab. Pea crabs, incidentally, often have a problem reproducing. Once the female is in a burrow she is reluctant to leave. The male therefore takes off from his burrow at certain times of the year and goes calling. He has to be even smaller than the female to get into the burrow with her. In fact, the males of some species are said to be so small that they have never been found.

Although neither of the ghost shrimp are considered edible by humans, alongside them in the muds and sands are some of the shellfish most highly prized by man. In Bolinas Lagoon there are acres of different clams, varying in size from the tiny *Gemma gemma* to the mighty geoduck, and including the big Washington clams which are so good for chowder, and the gapers and succulent littlenecks.

Clams work their way down into the muds and sands to find a favorable location where they may stay for several years. They have two sets of siphons, one to take in food—they feed on detritus—the other to dispose of waste. The giant geoduck, *Panope generosa*, contains both siphons in a common tube which may be thirty inches long. The geoduck's body often weighs ten or twelve pounds, and is so large that the clam cannot get the two halves of its shell together. Once very common in the tidal flats at Bolinas, geoducks have been removed in such numbers that only a few now remain.

From the New York bight
southward, great coastal plain
estuaries rim the continent and
the land is lapped by warmer
waters from the Gulf Stream. In
the Gulf of Mexico, the...coast is
swampy in many places, with
lush bayous.

Some clams can live a long time, growing ever larger and consequently enlarging the holes for their siphons. One biologist uses a handy scale to measure their ages: a hole big enough for one finger indicates a ten-year-old clam; a two-finger hole, a fifteen-year-old; a three-finger hole, a twenty-year-old.

Both exotic and indigenous oysters live in Bolinas Lagoon. A few imports from Japan remain from an unsuccessful commercial oyster-seeding a few years ago. (Exotics are frequently introduced into estuaries. Some, like these oysters, are brought in purposefully. Most, however, arrive by chance, being carried on the hulls, or in the ballast water, of ships. Ships link the world's flora and fauna as well as its ports.) An interesting native species, *Ostrea lurida*, once prized by the Indians, grows in rocky areas. This bivalve changes its sex each year, being alternately male and female. Oysters send out clouds of eggs and sperm simultaneously in the early summer months and seem often to be programmed to release them on neap tides so that the sex cells will have a chance to meet. The fertilized egg becomes a veliger, a small larva with two hairy lobes that enable it to swim. Veligers somehow know to move upstream to avoid being washed out to sea. Oysters reproduce in enormous numbers, some producing several millions of eggs a year. The few veligers that survive fasten themselves onto some solid substrate, often the shell of a dead ancestor. Thus are oyster beds seeded naturally.

Like other filter feeders, oysters are well equipped to concentrate various minerals and nutrients—as well as poisons—contained in the detritus they eat. In polluted waters, they may become highly contaminated with harmful bacteria. Relocated in pure water, they soon decontaminate themselves

Bolinas Lagoon is home for many other mollusks, for cockles and whelks and, on its sandspit, for the huge snail *Tethys californicus*, called the seahare. This extraordinary animal carries its shell inside, and can grow to a weight of fifteen or more pounds browsing on seaweed alone. The seahare is hermaphroditic and can be either male or female—or both—when it copulates.

The nudibranch, frequently called a sea slug, is another mollusk without a visible shell. One of the most beautiful, *Hermissenda crassicornis*, crawls along the bottom of the estuary in search of hydroids, its preferred food. To make up for its lack of protective armor, the nudibranch sometimes retains the stinging cells—nematocysts—from the hydroids it eats and uses them against its own enemies. It can also produce a most unpleasant smell when alarmed, and can squirt out colored fluid. It is thought that nudibranchs make disagreeable eating, for they are mostly left alone by larger predators.

In the mud of the small pools on the island in Bolinas Lagoon live colonies of tiny snails with towering shells, *Cerithidea californica*. In winter, they appear in armies, wearing on their shells an orangey fuzz of algal growth. They glide along, scraping other algae from the pool's bottom with their sharp tongues. *Littorina scutulata*, the checkered periwinkle, also occurs on the island. And on its sandy shores and on the estuary's sand spit the inch-sized *Olivella biplicata*, a beautiful purple and olive snail, travels just under the surface of the sand, feeding on the diatoms there, and leaving above an intricate pattern of the tunnels it has made.

Far more agile than the slow-moving snails are the small crabs that inhabit the island. *Hemigrapsus oregensis* and *Pachygrapsus crassipes* occur in great numbers. Shy little animals, they hurry into their burrows —which pock the channel banks—at the first sound or sight of an intruder. They are favored food of certain shorebirds, and need to be nimble to escape their pursuers.

Evidently they evade the sharks and rays that lurk along the shore, but many other crustaceans are not so lucky and end up as food for these fish. The shark and the ray belong to an intermediate evolutionary group, being neither soft-bodied nor bony; their skeletons are made of cartilage. The rays have unusual talents. They can dig ditches on the substrate as wide as their "wing-stretch," about four feet. They flap their wings against the mud, pulling out such hapless creatures as the fat innkeeper.

The true bony fishes come into Bolinas Lagoon in successive waves, species following species. They use the estuary on a selective basis. The rainbow trout—the prized steelhead—spawn in the stream and are common from December to May. The trout are followed by the staghorn sculpin which are found in greatest number between May and January. Aside from being home to the anadromous silver salmon, which arrive in February or March, the stream itself produces a good crop of fresh water fish —roaches (the fish, in this case) and sticklebacks. Striped bass linger in its deeper pools in late spring and early summer, and smelt may turn up then, too.

The anadromous fish employ the estuary as a pressure chamber where they adjust their internal pressure to either salt or fresh water, depending on which direction they happen to be heading. Some larger fish of the open sea, such as the herring, use the estuary as a dining room. They chase in schools of smaller fish, such as anchovies, then remain in the estuary to feast. As a nursery, however, the estuary performs one of its most important functions. Swarms of larvae and juvenile fish are found in its deeper waters. They graze on algae or eat small crustaceans, clams, worms, or the rich detritus. The young of many fish taken commercially—sanddabs and sole, flounder and turbot— come into the estuary and stay to fatten up while they are growing. Rockfish, blenny, perch and cabezon may come and go with the tides. More than thirty species in all use Bolinas Lagoon at one time or another during their lives.

A number of mammals use the estuary occasionally; some live permanently among its salt marshes. On the east coast, porpoises relish the estuary's fiddler crabs and clams. Porpoises are charming creatures, friendly and unafraid, delighted to travel alongside the prow of a boat. Considered among the most intelligent of the mammals, this animal has nevertheless failed to figure out one critical problem—how to avoid the nets cast out for albacore, one of its favorite foods. Fishermen who haul up porpoises at sea often kill them or leave them to die on the deck. So great is the loss of its numbers that the porpoise is regarded an endangered species.

At Bolinas Lagoon, the sand strand of the salt marsh is home for many small furry mammals such as voles and field mice. They eat the seeds of the grasses and pickleweed and the conifers. Occasionally a deer swims across the channel to browse on the plants. Sometimes there are tracks of raccoons in the mud. But the most enchanting mammals are the harbor seals. I sometimes walk to within viewing distance of their pod on the island. They know how to relax. They spread out in the sunshine on their backs or stomachs, or loll comfortably on one another. They are keen of hearing and wary. One step too close and they make their way quickly into the water, submerge, and reappear only when well offshore.

The pups, whelped here in springtime, are full of curiosity. A friend of mine traveling in a canoe once surprised a pup offshore. The young animal swam right up to him, ready to get acquainted. The mother seal (or an adult family friend), being wiser, swam rapidly over, slipped beneath the pup, lifted it onto her back, and promptly carried it off to safety. My friend swears that the mother turned and gave the pup a long hard dis-approving look—a warning on the danger of taking up with people.

The estuary's living world does not end, of course, at the surface of its waters or its tidal flats or marshes. Much of it begins where the shore birds, the gulls, the sea birds, and wildfowl find their food and shelter. They fill vital niches in the estuary's community and are essential to the complex web of life it supports. And, unlike the animals of the estuary's unseen world, the birds are visible and beautiful, ours to wonder at and to enjoy.

5. The aerial world

On a morning in late September, a thin fog drifts through Bolinas Lagoon. Against the horizon it makes a dull gray band, but overhead it is soft and gleaming and has the irridescent quality of opals. The sun is low, appearing like a lead disc, pale and cold as the moon.

I walk along the seaward side of the island. Long runners of saltgrass form a stiff web over the sands. The bunchgrass has dried into big rosy tufts. Bright yellow blooms of *Grindelia* are incandescent in the mist. The purplish cruciform blossoms of the delicate sea rocket, *Cakile,* have now formed into fat seed pods. I stop to admire this modest plant, knowing that inside those pods are four seeds, two programmed to regenerate when wetted by fresh water, two ready to grow when the water is brackish. The sea rocket will survive.

The higher shore is wet and carved by the retreating waters into deep ripples. In the depressions formed by them, the drift of the sea and the land is caught and held. There are shells, broken and bleached dead white. There are bits of seaweed, small purple carapaces of crabs washed in from the reef offshore, dried twisted grasses, and shards of wood worn smooth by the waves. Lower on the shore and to the south are the little mounds built by the ghosts shrimp and the fat innkeeper, hillocks of dark gray mud thrown up onto the brown of the coarser sand.

There are footprints of birds everwhere, some very large, some showing the imprint of webbed feet, some small and sharp and strung out in long attenuated patterns. There are tiny holes where small beaks have probed, too, and splashes of white droppings on the wet sands. The birds themselves are all around me. From the marsh, I hear a constant chorus of gentle calls. It is almost impossible to see the birds in the faded grasses, so soft is the dun gray of their folded wings. Offshore stand two herons, appearing black in the fog. They are watching me. When I come too close they take off with a loud flap of their wings and a raucous *aark-aark-aark.*

Along the water's edge, a lone sandpiper lands with wings held high and stiff, takes a few steps and starts to probe the wet sand. I startle it and the bird runs with wings lifted, then beats them hard until airborne. I watch a young western gull chase a plover that has a choice morsel of food. The smaller bird races furiously along the wave's edge, stops briefly to gulp down its food, then begins to probe the sand nonchalantly, ignoring its pursuer. The gull slows down, then stalks the plover, hoping for a leftover. A small crowd of dunlin circles and then settles down on a muddy stretch of shore. I watch one of the birds pull out an annelid worm as neatly as a robin extracts an earthworm from my lawn at home. The dunlin clearly like to travel together. Moved by some mysterious mechanism, they take off in perfect unison, circle again and drift down on the other side of the marsh.

Three brown pelicans come in from the sea. They stroke the air with strong wings, glide a long distance, then stroke the air once more. They skim the waves so closely it seems they must dip into them, but they never do. Their great heads are pulled back in flight, necks curved like the herons! A duck passes them in rapid, nervous flight. A half dozen cormorants scud by, holding their long black bodies straight and parallel to the water. A long-billed curlew, a tawny velvety gold, passes over with a whistling *pleet, pleet, pleet* from its downcurved beak. A marbled godwit stands just offshore in the shallows. It dips its whole body up and down, like a pump in an oil field, but far more purposefully. Nearby, a phalarope spins like a slow top as it feeds in the water.

I round the corner of the island and walk through wet marshland. The water is seeping in slowly, silently invading the small clumps of pickle-weed. Ahead, I see the cormorants standing on the shore with their wings stretched out, feathers dripping. The pelicans are with them, looking dignified with their long solemn faces. A raft of gulls is spread out on a sandy bar just offshore, next to the pod of seals. The seals watch me without moving.

I walk on into the marsh to a small pool, a salt pan flooding deeper now as the tide comes in. A greater yellowlegs is bobbing for fish. This is an elegant bird with light gray back, white belly, long black bill, and tall yellow legs. The pool is quiet but for the bird and the little water striders that scurry over its glassy surface.

I stop a moment, aware that once more I am being watched. Two brown-streaked owls sitting on a rise in the marsh practically impale me with their fierce yellow eyes. As I walk on by they remain motionless, except for their heads, which swivel slowly to keep me in full view. Suddenly the owls take off in curious floppy flight, not holding their bodies level as other birds do, but pumping them up and down with every wing stroke. They are short-eared owls, returned early this year—probably from Alaska—to winter on the marsh. Alert for the bright-eyed voles that tunnel through the grasses on the higher parts of the island, these owls also hunt the shorebirds here, choosing the dunlin most often for their prey.

At the shore I let the water creep higher on my rubber boots. The fog is burning off in a kind of smoky radiance and the sun comes through at first in a weak wash of light and then in a good warm spill. The last of the mist steams off the wet sands. The birds grow quieter now in the new warmth—and there are hundreds around me.

As I turn to walk toward the channel, it occurs to me that birds play a little noticed but critical role in the workings of the ecosphere. In their myriad webs of flight, they alone among living creatures bind the earth together. In their short flights over the land, they stitch together the forests, marshes and mountains. In their arcs across the great reaches of water, they join together the distant parts of the sea, tying islands to mainlands and continent to continent. And in their migratory travels, they string their flyways between all the wetlands of the world, between the bays and estuaries, the river valleys and the shores. They bridge the equator to link the very ends of the planet.

Bolinas Lagoon lies on the great Pacific Flyway. Although it is only three square miles in size, the wealth of its tidelands and marshes and shorelands provides essential support for tens of thousands of birds. It is a layover place for countless migrants, the nesting ground for many land birds, and one of the last remaining breeding areas on the Pacific Coast for the great blue heron and the American egret. The estuary is also winter quarters for a variety of shorebirds and waterfowl. In the course of a year, it may be used by nearly a hundred and fifty different species in all.

The birds share the bounty of the place with a kind of innate efficiency. Different species fit themselves into different niches, occupying each part of the wetlands, the water and the shore, using for food the whole spectrum of plant and animal and insect life that is here. Although only a few species remain the year around, as the seasons swing there is an ever-changing procession of winged visitors; flock follows flock, arriving at its chosen time, lingering or passing through. Each species moves to its own rhythm. There is a deeper, elemental rhythm, too, to the tides of migration. In the late winter and spring when the rains bring down nutrients from the land into the estuary and new life awakens on the shores and in the water, the avian life also swells to a climax. There may be thousands of birds using the estuary and the land around it before the end of April. In early summer, when the days stretch out long and warm and dry, the estuary rests, and there are fewer birds. But the place is never empty of them, never silent of the sound of wings and calls and song.

Many land birds fequent the canyons and meadows and ridges around the estuary. There are waders—the herons and egrets; and soarers—the hawks, vultures and ospreys; but the greatest number are perchers, or Passerines. Most of the perching birds have innately beautiful balance and curving feet which can grasp and hang onto things. They swing on the reeds of the fresh-water marsh, or sit easily on twigs and branches along the brushy shore, and on the limbs of alders, eucalyptus, buckeyes and pine. They rest on their perches, watch for their prey, or pour out their songs of courtship.

The land birds are often colored more brightly than flowers. Hummingbirds glint gold and red and green in the sun. Swallows shine green and purple. Red-winged blackbirds flash crimson shoulders, and the jays are a deeper blue than the water or the sky. Some land birds, like the quail, the wrens and the owls, are more quietly shaded, streaked with soft browns that blend them into the brush and grasses.

Throughout the eons that the birds have flown, they have watched the earth evolve and the continents take shape. They have felt the cold winds off the great glaciers, and survived. They have witnessed the emergence of forests and flowers, of mammoths and men.

Land birds are apt to be catholic eaters. The western meadowlark that sings from the island, for instance, feasts on seeds and insects and small aquatic life as well. But the swallows that dip and glide and sweep so gracefully on their slim pointed wings are insectivores: they hunt on the wing, opening their mouths wide to trap their prey. The dark phoebes that live along the streams are also expert at catching flying insects, preferring to snap their food from the air.

Not surprisingly, many of the land birds here prefer wet places. The barn swallows, the cliff swallows and the purple martins need mud to build their nests. And the savannah sparrow is very much at home in the salt marsh. It has the unexpected ability to excrete excess salt from its body after drinking brine or brackish water.

The shorebirds are very different in appearance and habit. They have evolved to use the tidelands and the shallows as well as the marshes. Most are a modest gray-brown, a good camouflage color for mud flats and sandy shores. Many have fine traceries or bold patterns of black and white markings which match the bits of drift along the scrimmage line of water and land. Almost all are darker on top than on their bellies. This countershading enables the birds to blend with ground shadows when the sun is high. Their protective coloration is so effective, in fact, that they are easy to overlook, even when present in great numbers. I have frequently driven along Bolinas Lagoon without noticing the shorebirds there. But when I stopped the car and looked with field glasses, I could see that the tidal flats were alive with the motion of feeding birds.

The shorebirds are well-equipped to feed in shallow waters and damp muds and sands. The legs of different species come in a remarkable assortment of lengths, enabling some birds to use high ground, and others to stand and wade comfortably in water of varying depth. The plovers (literally "birds of the rain" or *pleuviers*) and the peeps, the motley tribe of sandpipers, work the upper levels of mud and sand. They are mostly pickers, having small, sharply-pointed beaks with which to snap up small crustaceans and other tidbits. Some larger shorebirds have highly specialized beaks. The lovely avocet has an upcurved bill to seine the water and wet mud, and may be seen swinging its head from side to side as it feeds. The beak of the long-billed curlew curves down to probe deep into the holes of crabs and ghost shrimp. The dowitcher has a special sense organ on the tip of its bill to nose out choice morsels in the mud. Although some shorebirds choose a mixed diet of plants and animals, most of them—including the very smallest—are carnivorous.

The sea birds and waterfowl that come to the estuary are equally specialized. Their legs may be short and powerful, and their webbed feet make efficient paddles. They are usually superb swimmers. The divers among them have legs set well back on their bodies so that they can tip forward easily. This, along with short legs, accounts for their waddling gait on land. Many have long supple necks that allow them to explore underwater while they float on the surface. Being great travelers, they have strong wings and are among the loveliest birds in flight. All but the luckless cormorants have a special gland which secretes oil to waterproof their coats. The water birds may often be seen preening, carefully lubricating every feather.

The shorebirds are well-equipped
to feed in shallow water and
damp muds and sands. The legs of
different species come in a
remarkable assortment of lengths,
enabling some birds…to stand
and wade comfortably in water of
varying depth.

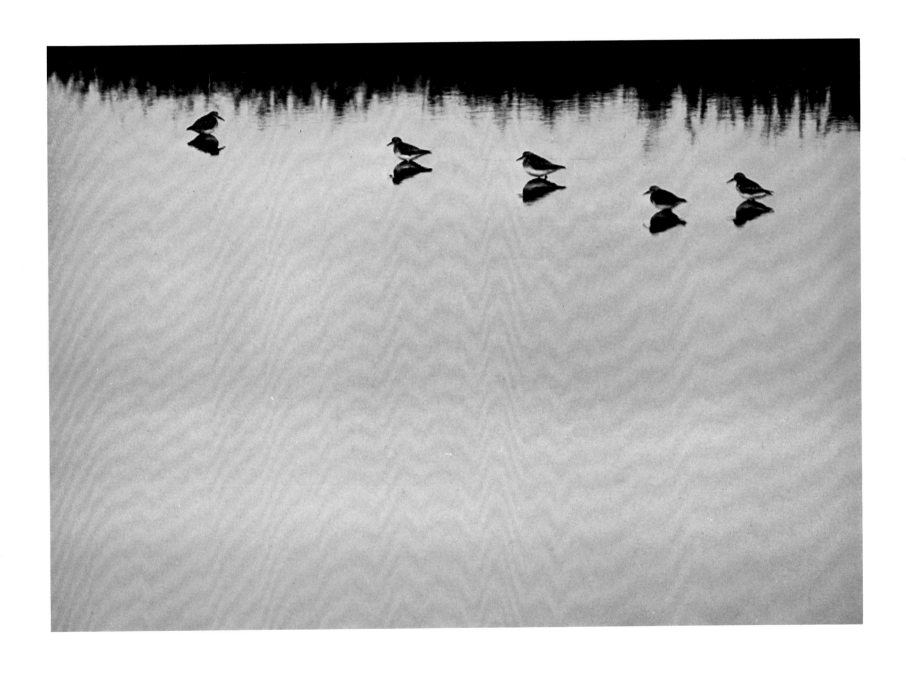

The variety of their bills is a testament to nature's ingenuity. There is the broad bill of the dabbling duck, which makes an excellent strainer; the fiercely hooked beak of the cormorant, a highly efficient tearing tool; the huge scoop of the pelican, which is held wide open when the bird hits the water; the serrated bill of the merganser, which can be swung sideways to trap fish—and all sorts of variations in between.

Many of the ducks are vegetarians, eating the algae in the estuary. But the diving ducks, the loons and grebes, the pelicans and the cormorants are all great fishermen. And the gulls eat anything and everything.

Bolinas Lagoon has few year-round avian residents, but certain species can nearly always be seen. Whenever I round the curve along the lagoon, I watch for jaunty kingfishers sitting on the telephone wires. The kingfishers have large crested heads, and dagger-like beaks to stab fish. In spring, these birds hollow out their nests in sandy cliffs above the beach some distance away. The females scream imprecations at anyone who strolls too close.

The brush and meadows here are home for many California quail, the male wearing his unmistakable ornament, a short black plume of feathers that curves forward over his head. Near the mouth of the estuary in a stand of cypress draped with gray-green lichen, black-crowned night herons roost by day, brooding silently. At twilight, they fly out to fish, crying out and answering one another with a hoarse *quawrk, quawrk, quawrk.*

A pair of osprey sometimes hovers above the estuary's waters. These beautiful large hawks need a high treetop to nest and a wide territory to hunt. I have not found their home, but on a spring afternoon I have seen one dive at great speed and seize a fish in its outstretched talons.

The sky almost always holds a red-tailed hawk, describing a wide circle as it soars, holding its body as still as a glider, its wide wings and round tail stretched taut. A vulture bent into a bread V may wheel nearby, appearing fierce until given chase by a smaller bird. The vulture flees ignominiously when challenged.

A dozen noisy killdeer make their nests on grassy hillocks near the shore each year. These handsomely patterned birds, colored rust and black and white, are devoted parents, dragging their wings in feigned injury and crying piteously if their young are threatened.

The most striking nesters here are the herons and egrets. The great blue heron has a wing span of almost six feet, and the common egret's is nearly as wide. When they spread their great wings and soar against a pale February sky, they are breath-taking to watch. These two species share the tidal channels where they fish, as well as the tops of the redwood trees which they have pruned flat while nesting in one particular canyon. The same birds return year after year to the same place, arriving in late winter to repair the storm damage to their nests. The male and female dance solemnly, and pass twigs back and forth before they place them carefully. In nuptial plumage, they trail long feathers that whip about like lacy capes in the breeze.

In the brief lull of quiet that comes to the estuary in the early summer, the herons and egrets are at their busiest. They must fish continuously to feed their clamoring offspring. Dozens of adults stand in the shallow water, still and exquisite. When a bird makes a successful catch, it flies unerringly for its tree-top nest.

Bit by bit, the world of the birds has been diminished. Although man no longer hunts so ruthlessly, he offers instead the threats of chemical poisoning, and — most devastating of all — the physical destruction of the birds' natural environments.

There are always a few migrant stragglers around Bolinas Lagoon. These are usually young birds that may stay the whole year, apparently unaware that they should be going somewhere else when the seasons change. A half dozen great blue herons remain every winter after their families have long since departed. Common loons and western grebes paddle about in summer waters, though they are normally winter visitors here. A few dozen willets with their bold black and white chevron-striped wings feed in the stands of pickleweed all year. A long-billed curlew or two, a pair of whimbrels, or a half dozen black-bellied plovers can nearly always be found in the salt marsh.

The place is never without gulls. In summer their flocks are spread all over the delta of the estuary's stream. In the amber days of September and October, they gather on the sand bar off the island, sharing it with harbor seals. The gulls snooze long hours away, all facing in the same direction, taking the warm breezes head on, preening and primping or resting their heads on their wings. In spring and winter, they may ride out the storms on the water, or move upland into the meadows, sailing aloft on the winds.

Although related to the shorebirds, the gulls are far more versatile. Their superb design, combining beauty and function, has served them so well it has not been modified for millions of years. With streamlined bodies and strong tapered beaks, they can dive from the air for food as expertly and successfully as their relatives, the terns. Their feet are webbed for strong swimming, even underwater. Placed mid-body, their legs are long enough to let them walk sure-footedly along the water's edge, where they look for food left by the tide.

In the air, gulls are truly superlative. Their long, pointed wings equip them to ride the winds, to soar and lift where air currents flow up over the shore, to hang motionless in the sky like large white flowers fastened to nothing. They can also travel purposefully, beating the air steadily with strong wings to attain speeds of as much as thirty-five miles per hour.

At first glance, all the gulls look alike. It is easy to assume that the same birds stay in the estuary year around. But most of the several species here are migratory. Some, like the herring gull, a large handsome dark-silver bird, are among the great wanderers of the world. These cosmopolitans are common throughout the Northern Hemisphere, being found in the Azores, the Mediterranean, Arabia, Central Africa and the Philippines. In North America, they use all the flyways. Those that visit Bolinas Lagoon may be en route to breeding grounds in Washington or Alaska, or headed for their wintering grounds in Baja California or El Salvador.

Another great traveler is the mew gull which winters here far from its breeding grounds in interior or north Alaska. The California gull is poorly named. It spends more time out of state than in, nesting on the Great Salt Lake in Utah, or Yellowstone Lake in Wyoming, or lingering on the high lakes of the Sierra Nevada until the storms of winter send it west to this coast.

In spring, small flocks of Bonaparte's gulls fly through, stopping only to feed and rest on their journey northward to breeding grounds in Alaska. This pure white gull with yellow bill wears a black cap in breeding plumage, and is the only dark-headed gull in the area, except for Heermann's gull which is black all over when immature. Heermann's beak is a startling

In the brief lull that comes to the estuary in the early summer, the herons and egrets must fish continuously to feed their clamoring offspring. They stand in the shallow water, still and exquisite.

red. This is the only gull — and indeed one of the few migratory birds — that flies south to breed.

The ring-billed gull and the western gull are frequent visitors. The western nests on nearby offshore islands. With a wing spread of two feet or more, this is a big bird. It has a handsome dark gray mantle, a sturdy white head, and a yellow bill. It likes to sit on an old log or piling close to land and sound off in a raucous voice.

Most migrants arrive and depart more obviously than the gulls do. Tides of land birds come through in spring. A few—such as the swallows, phoebes, and many sparrows—remain to nest, but most stay only briefly and continue on their way. Far more spectacular in number and variety are the migrating shorebirds and wildfowl which use Bolinas Lagoon. At the time of the summer solstice, I watch for the first arrivals.

One day in early July, a small flock of western sandpipers, perhaps ninety birds or so, appears like a puff of dark smoke on the northern sky. Growing in size, the puff thins out into tiny fliers that wheel in perfect synchronization as though fastened together into a shimmering mesh, then twirled and shaken by an unseen hand. Now dark against the sky, now showing their underbodies in a white glimmer, they pirouette down, fold their wings and rest.

These are the heralds of the great procession of winged visitors that will follow, a growing extravaganza of wild birds coming in ever-increasing waves out of the northern skies. First the shorebirds and then the waterfowl — dozens of different species — will find and use the estuary in the next few months. Some will stop only to feed and rest; some will spend the winter here.

The western sandpipers swell in number as July moves on. The birds stay long enough to fatten up, and then continue on their way south. Before autumn ends, several thousand will have left the temporary imprint of their small feet on the tidal flats. On their return in the spring, ten thousand or more may congregate at a time, filling the marshes to their limits.

Following them in July — and often flying in at night — will be the least sandpipers. These are the smallest of the peeps, each bird weighing only an ounce or so. They are agile at probing the higher tidal flats for tiny animals, chattering as they feed. The adults come in a good five to six weeks before the immature. They often spend the winter. While here, they will molt into their brighter plumage, readying themselves to breed when they return northward in the spring.

On through August and September, the sandpipers wing in. The dowitchers, among the larger members of the tribe, love the heights of the skies. They arrive in great assemblies, calling to one another as they come. On the ground, they are more silent and move about with quick steps. In their anxiety to get at their food, they often duck their heads completely under the water as they probe in the shallows. The dunlin come late. They have begun their molt in the arctic and many will finish it here during the golden days of Indian summer.

Along with the plovers and turnstones, the sandpipers are the greatest avian travelers of all the migrants. In leap-frog migration, many of these shorebirds fly enormous distances, bested only by the arctic tern which flies

The herons and egrets share the tidal channels where they fish, as well as the tops of the redwood trees which they have pruned flat while nesting. The same birds return to the estuary year after year.

Wild birds come in ever-increasing waves out of the northern skies. First the shorebirds and then the waterfowl—dozens of different species will use the estuary in the next few months to feed and rest.

from the northern to the southern polar region and back each year (but rarely chooses the Pacific Coast). The golden plover, passing through this estuary in the fall, is one of a breed that may fly twenty-four hundred miles nonstop across the ocean. The black-bellied plover, common here in winter in his gray plumage, is found from arctic coasts to the southern hemisphere, and may travel as much as fifteen thousand miles a year in round trip flight. The ruddy turnstone, a rapid flier and ingenious feeder that tips over pebbles to surprise whatever may lurk beneath, comes through in fall and spring, en route from as far north as Alaska to his wintering grounds, which may be in Peru. A lesser yellowlegs, flying along this shore, may have bred her young on a quiet and lonely lake in the heart of Alaska's Brooks Range.

Although they are more modest travelers, the waterfowl and sea birds which share Bolinas Lagoon with the shorebirds as the autumn days grow shorter have often come thousands of miles themselves. The pintail ducks, slim birds with graceful lines, pass through in fall bound for California's Central Valley. The close-knit flocks of cinnamon teals that twist and turn in swift flight, likely started in British Columbia and will winter in Nevada. American widgeons, with their wild musical call, pass by in flocks of three, stopping to bob and pivot on the estuary's water, sitting bouyantly and taking off in perpendicular flight, like small helicoptors. Bound from Alaska they will winter further south, and pass this way again next spring.

The diving ducks frequently use this estuary as the terminus of their long flight from the north. The buffleheads fly in silently on a fall day, without the sweet whistling sound that signals the flight of many other ducks. They land with a splash and skid along the surface to a standstill. With large black heads and white eye patches, they are easy to spot bobbing on the water. The larger white-winged scoters fly in from sea Indian file. Great fishermen, these ducks are expert underwater swimmers and deep divers. Their flight is heavy and labored. Like a big plane, the bird requires a long runway to land. And when taking off it must patter along the surface for some distance before lumbering into the air.

Occasionally in the early winter twilight, whistling swans may wing overhead in a large V. The leader, it is thought, cleaves the air as the prow of a ship cleaves the water, sending back the strong inverted V-shaped ripple on which the following birds may rest their outer wings. The swans may be seen changing sides in flight, presumably to rest one wing and then the other, and the leader, finally exhausted, may drop to the rear to rest and let another take its place.

Although the black brant, which breed in Alaska, use this flyway on their travels south, I have seen them most often on their return in the spring. Wave after wave may come through during late April or early May. The black brant flies most often in small flocks, winging low over the water in a single swift line which lifts and falls in graceful undulations. On the water it rides high with head and tail uplifted, showing the white stripe on its throat and its pale undertail-coverts. Sometimes these geese leave the estuary in pairs or foursomes, heading for a more favored spot nearby where the eelgrass streams in the tidal waters.

I have stood in the long twilight of a wet spring evening, watching three black brant flying with strong and rapid wing strokes through a fine scudding mist. Their direction northward was sure, their flight even and purposeful. They knew where they were going. They brought to mind a belief of Einstein's (for which he was derided), that birds sense a band of force unknown to us, and use it to find their way above the long windy slope of the earth.

Of all the birds that come to the estuary, my favorite is the sanderling. Consider this diminutive sandpiper that probes the sands with frantic haste and careens as though on roller skates at the edge of the waves. Scarcely larger than a thistle—and weighing not much more—the sanderling travels the winds of the world, follows wavelines on open shores and in estuaries, chases the retreating waters of every continent. These dauntless birds ring the Arctic Circle for a few brief weeks in early summer to mate and nest and rear their young. Then they flock out, bound for New Zealand and Chile, as well as Florida and California.

This migratory pattern may demand of the sanderling that it spend much of its time traveling, except for the few brief weeks of early arctic summer when it stops to breed. Into this short breeding period the bird must cram the duties of a lifetime if it is to perpetuate its species. It must act with alacrity and success, and live with incredible intensity. And in ways that we can only dimly fathom, these tiny birds are programmed to do just that. In a sense, they epitomize the wonder and the mystery of all the birds that wing their way to the far places of the earth to mate and nest and rear their young.

The flocks of sanderlings that leave Bolinas Lagoon in spring follow a pathway known only to themselves as they head for the arctic slope. Once there, the males establish their territories on the tundra. The ensuing courtship follows a strict and undeviating pattern of sanderling etiquette. By this mechanism of ritualized courtship, common to all birds, sanderlings discourage interbreeding with other species. Until paired, the male sanderling indulges in continuous flight display against the pale arctic sky, rising on vibrating wings and pouring forth a whole concert of sounds. The female watches him glide and quiver and trace small spirals in the sky and then herself may soar silently, while he sits to watch. Once paired, the two are inseparable for a time. Where one flies the other follows, as though they were ribboned together.

Before the final union the pair builds a nest, a deep cup into which bits of dry willow leaves and dryas and lichens, the modest flora of the tundra, may blow. The male nudges his mate to leave this arctic bower and they run together in a curious prenuptial dance, side by side, rubbing against each other until the male stops to push his bill against his mate's breast. She stands quiescent while he mounts her, wings fluttering, pulls her crown and nape feathers with his bill, and consummates the union.

Forgetting their earlier nest, the two build a second one now, finding a site near a saxifrage or willow, but always open to the nightless June sky. Soon the female will preen herself and lay the first of four emerald-green eggs, dropping the others in the next four or five days. Then the marriage is finished. The pair-bond is dissolved, and either the male or female assumes the role of single parent while the partner takes off for parts unknown.

For the next three to four weeks the parent sanderling broods the eggs, each shaped like a wedge of pie and kept in pie-order so that the bird can

Owls on a rise in the marsh practically impale me with their fierce eyes. They are alert for the voles that tunnel through the grasses.

cover them with its body. Through the endless days, the small bird sits and preens and fusses with its feathers or sleeps through the cooler hours, sometimes escaping briefly into the sky to perform a few aerial acrobatics. The brood is hatched in a matter of hours. The chicks, no more than puffs of downy feathers, may crawl out of the nest and stumble around when only three hours old. In a day, they will leave the nest for good to follow their parent. Less than three weeks later, the young birds are flying strongly, their down feathers already giving way to juvenile plumage. By late July they will have increased their weight sevenfold to tip the scales at a good two ounces. By mid-August, the adult birds have left on the long flight southward, perhaps bound for a stopover in our estuary on their journey. By mid-September the young have followed. The breeding ground is empty.

If all goes well for those small voyagers, they will return in another spring to the same area where they were born, and repeat the sanderling ritual. But first they will fly through the darkening autumn skies, down the whole long curve of the earth, following its coasts and wetlands across the equator, wheeling and turning against the dawn, against the evening, choosing in some mysterious way a pathway, knowing innately the journey they must make, carrying within those tiny bodies a certain knowledge of the stars and what the wind means and how the earth turns.

What sends these migratory flocks through the skies to follow the great arc of the planet, to mate and nest and rear their young, and then return for a few brief weeks to a winter home? Perhaps they follow a pattern imposed throughout millions of years of evolution by the great cataclysmic changes in climate, the succession of ice ages that periodically locked the northern hemisphere in glaciers. Perhaps they are only exploiting the avian food supply of the earth. Perhaps they move for another stranger, stronger reason unknown to us. Whatever the reason, as the winter days grow longer the migratory birds of the estuary are gripped by a deep imperious urge. Then, braving great dangers, the fury of storms and winds which may dash them against the land or into the sea, crossing over barren places, avoiding the lethal artifacts of man—his buildings, his transmitters, his blinding beacons—the birds fly unerringly to their destinations.

How these scraps of life, all wing and eye and furiously beating heart, navigate the reaches of the earth is not entirely known to us. We do know that their vision far surpasses that of man, and that they have remarkable visual memory, carrying as it were a cerebral map of the land along their flyways. We know that they use landmarks—a mountain range, a river valley, a forest, or a wetland—to guide themselves. We believe that they sense great unseen waves of pressure in the air, the weather fronts, and that they may time their coming and going by the advent of seasonal storms. We know that they use the sun by day and the stars by night, charting their courses over the earth as sailors have long charted their courses across the seas. We conjecture, too, that somehow—perhaps in the cells of their blood—they are equipped to use the earth's magnetic field, and orient their flights accordingly. We know that they may gain great altitudes—some riding the jet streams—and that they travel when they chose, often at night, when a fortunate watcher may see their silhouettes against a bright moon, or hear their faint cries, musical and lonesome, drifting down from the dark skies.

We know that the migrants store up fat on their breasts to use as fuel, and that some can travel for days without stopping, but that others must rest and replenish their fuel in the wetlands that lay along their way.

And we know that in preparation for their long flights, the migrants store up fat on their breasts to use as fuel, and that some can travel for days without stopping, but that others must rest and replenish their fuel in the wetlands that lay along their way.

I am reminded of such things when I see a pair of snowy egrets standing on the shore, their white plumes streaming in a stiff spring breeze. Or when I surprise a raft of mergansers, arrived unseen during an autumn night, their rakish horizontal crests ruffled by the onshore wind. Or when I see the first brown pelicans arrive in mid-July, planing down in a long uneven V toward their haunt near the seals on the island.

As I watch the pelicans fold themselves into comfortable sleeping shapes, heads resting on their backs, eyes closed, I am also reminded that these big birds have been around for millions of years. Pelicans flew through Eocene skies, 65 million years ago. And shorebirds, too, were probing the muds and sands of that period. Through all the millennia since then, and indeed since long before, birds have provided an essential link in countless life cycles. In and on their bodies, they have carried the eggs of fish and the seeds of plants along every shore and inland as well. They have pollinated the flowers of every century and broadcast the pollen of conifers from cones on which they perched. Sea birds have taken the riches of the sea into their bodies, concentrated them, and dropped them as guano onto its rocks. Shorebirds have harvested the bounty of the wetlands and, with land birds, helped to circulate nutrients to every corner of the earth.

And throughout the eons that the birds have flown, they have watched the earth evolve and the continents take shape. They have felt the cold winds off the great glaciers, and survived. They have witnessed the emergence of forests and flowers, of mammoths and men. Until man came, the greatest danger to birds was the earth's changing climate and geography. But man proved to be a more dangerous agent of destruction. As a hunter, he has brought about the extinction—or near extinction—of many species.

"North America at one time probably contained more wildfowl than any other country of the globe, and even in the recollection of some living, the birds came down from the northland during the autumn in numbers that were incredible, promising a continuation of the race forever. I have, myself, seen great masses of ducks, and also of geese, rise at one time from the water in so dense a cloud as to obscure the sky, and every suitable water-covered spot held some members of the family throughout our limits. But these great armies of wildfowl will be seen no more in our land, only the survivors of their broken ranks."

This description was written in 1898 by D. G. Elliot. It has poignance now when the small flocks of autumn wildfowl arrive at Bolinas Lagoon—when we consider a few hundred, or a thousand, birds of a species to be something of a wonder.

Bit by bit, the world of the birds has been diminished. Although man no longer hunts so ruthlessly, he offers instead the threats of chemical poisoning, and—most devastating of all—the physical destruction of the birds' natural environments. In fact, many birds which use the estuaries—such as the clapper rail, the brown pelican and the savannah sparrow—are now rare or endangered species.

Every time a wetland is drained, a marsh is diked, a lagoon is filled, an estuary is poisoned, there is one less place for the migratory flocks to visit. As the birds seek new places to rest and feed, and do not find them, they become lost to the world. And the shock of their loss spreads out like waves of sound from a bell tolling.

Part II:
The edge of life

6. The spiral and the star

We are born with a need to wonder. Children feel it keenly. They share it with certain fortunate adults—with wise men and poets and scholars, and with those who know the earth intimately, watch night skies, or respond to the quickening of the seasons. It is wondering which has led us to push forever past the next horizon, to climb the highest mountain, to probe beneath the sea, to touch the moon and reach beyond. And always and most profoundly, it has led us to question our own being, our beginnings and the beginning of life on this small blue-green planet that is our home.

Man did his first wondering in wildness with an innocent mind, having no past to trouble him, and no answers. The world was new and fresh to him then and full of magic. Perhaps he began to wonder in the dim green light of a primeval forest when he listened with sudden curiosity to the conversation of birds, or stooped to trace with an exploring finger the tight-coiled spiral of an uncurling fern. Perhaps it was when he first made fire, or when he noticed how the sky was starred and how the sun and moon pursued their changing courses.

One unknown day he took the pathway of the river to the sea and found a new place, neither land nor water, but a commingling of the two. He must have stood there bewildered, blinded by the warm dazzle of sun on shallow water, hearing the wild cries of strange birds and feeling for the first time the elemental pull of the tide in the shifting sands beneath his feet. He may have turned back or pushed on through, but maybe he stopped to linger, feeling the richness and beauty of the place, feeling a sense of homecoming, belonging as he always and ultimately has to the sea and river as well as to the land. Surely he felt new questions quicken in his mind, hearing those birds, feeling that tide swing out, seeing the spiraled sea shells fastened to the fronds of grasses streaming in the water.

We do our wondering differently now. Our world is older, with too much of its magic gone. Our primeval forests are mostly cut down. Fire is as ordinary to us as striking a match. Our stars are dimmed by the lights of cities.

The places where our rivers meet the sea are all too often rearranged or poisoned. And we have lost most of our innocence, being heir to more knowledge than anyone can comprehend in a single lifetime. We now have vast libraries and millions of bookfuls of answers. We have gleaming laboratories, test tubes, tools of a sharpness too fine to measure, and machines of frightening abilities. We have trained minds, scientific rigor, and most ingenious techniques to explore the universe along with the smallest scrap of living matter. In the polished mirrors of giant telescopes we can catch the image of stars so deep in space their light has travelled billions of years to reach us. In the green-gold glow of the electron microscope we can examine the exquisite structure of viruses and probe for the secrets of the single cell. We trace our spirals now in galaxies of distant stars and in the hearts of cells.

And between the star and the cell we finger an infinitely delicate edge, the invisible line that separates the living from the unliving world. For we have found that the stuff of life is the stuff of stars. Elements most common in the universe—carbon, hydrogen, oxygen, and nitrogen—are the most common elements in every living thing on earth. Strung together in intricately ordered filaments, in ringed skeins, in tight-coiled springs and helixes, these elements form giant molecules of protein and nucleic acid, the mysterious substances that order all of life. In the sunlit cells of plants, these molecules make food from the energy of the sun. In the cells of man, they employ the energy of plants to fuel the beat of the human heart. And in every living cell, in delicately linked spirals of nucleic acid, the magic star-stuff which we call DNA, there is encoded the secret formula that programs the cell's existence and carries the blueprint of its progeny.

How could it happen? How did life come to be? How did the dust of dead stars assume the shape of flowers? The wings of wild birds? Curled ferns and spiraled sea shells? The human mind that wonders?

For all we have learned, we are as mute as the most innocent early man before these ultimate questions. But with what we know we can speculate now as he never could, with some things clear, a few certainties, a few pieces of the grand puzzle fitted into place. We can postulate a sequence of events that leads from the star to the living cell, and we can consider the estuary as the possible site of life's genesis.

Our point of beginning must be arbitrary, for life as we know it is part of a grand cosmic evolution which commenced at an unknown point in time. But we may choose the moment when earth—a small planet that circles a small star in a small galaxy that is only one of millions of galaxies in the universe—first spun into being, an act of evolution itself.

It was formed of the shining dust of nebulae and exploded stars. First an incandescent globe wrapped in a thick cloud of gasses (much as the planet Jupiter may be even now), it assumed mysteriously increasing order. Spinning and compacting, it began to cool, its heavier elements falling together to make a molten core, a thin crust forming on its surface. It was a world of flame and ceaseless storms, of steel-blue streaks of lightning, of glowing lava that streamed over drab rocks, and of fierce hot winds. Water formed in the sheath of gasses and poured down endlessly, much of it steaming off the naked earth but more and more of it surging and gullying across the raw forming landscape to feed the beginnings of the sea.

As the earth grew cooler its crust thickened and warped up into hills and mountains, folded itself, and warped up again. The clouds thinned out and sunlight poured down like a wash of fire in the full spectrum of its radiance, for there was no atmosphere as we know it, no free oxygen nor veil of ozone. Storms continued, and young rivers began to cut channels, shaping and scouring the restless land. And where the rivers met the growing sea, primitive estuaries formed and filled with sediments and formed again as the land pushed up. In the estuaries the particles of the land and the sediments of the sea made thick oozes and clays, compounds with magic in them.

As the eons passed, new and strange things began to happen in the rich brew of the primordial waters. Atoms of hydrogen and carbon, oxygen and nitrogen began to make tiny chains, arranged already in powerful patterns. They formed the simplest amino-acids, the elemental building blocks of life. And the tides pulled the waters against the shores and then drew them back, leaving behind the drift of the sea. Where the waters beat against the rough young rocks, the fragments of pre-life were scattered. But in the quieter parts of the estuaries, the waves left the sea's drift more gently to sink into the rich clays and oozes of the tidal flats.

How many times the waves stroked patiently over those primeval tidal flats we do not know, nor how many estuaries formed and filled and formed again. It was an infinitely slow alchemy, with the repeated wetting of the sea, and the sunlight shattering on the wet clays, and the earth sending out its radiant forces, and the lightning stabbing those shores. And always there were the encounters of amino-acids, those magic scraps made of the dust of stars; they met and parted and met again, until, caught by the estuaries' clay particles and held in that primordial ooze, they began to assume new forms.

In that world of sun and rock and water and patient moving sea, certain tides pulled down and left behind the shape of life, a gift of the universe, within the estuaries. At first it was nothing, a scrap, a speck, a microscopic blob of jelly. But at the same time, it was everything. Tiny, tough, mindless, it had the ability to survive, to nourish itself on the world around it, to grow and multiply and change and become a million different living things. The stuff of stars had become the stuff that would be man.

The earth was young, we think, less than a quarter of its present age when the miracle occurred. There was no witness, of course, and no trace of that first life has yet been found. But we know that there was a particular place where the particles of life came together and were linked and bound. And we surmise that it was in the warm ooze of the estuary. In rich colloidal clays, in the quiet reaches of tidal flats where the sea came flooding in each day, the elements of the land and ocean and river and star came together, joined in mysterious order into a living thing.

The estuary is a place for us to look at once again, a place in which to regain our sense of wonder.

There are numerous secrets sealed inside the earth. In sedimentary rocks laid down in ancient estuaries and shallow seas, in the gravels of river beds,

Man did his first wondering in wildness with an innocent mind, having no past to trouble him, and no answers. The world was new and fresh to him then and full of magic....We do our wondering differently now. Our world is older, with too much of its magic gone.

in peat bogs, in ancient marshes, in folds of lava, beneath layers of tuff and pumice spewed out by volcanoes—in countless crannies of the land—there is an extraordinary record of life once spawned and succoured and sometimes destroyed. The evidence may be only a tooth or a shard of bone, the delicate frond of a fossil fern, a footprint pressed into once-wet mud, a flake of obsidian, a shell bead, or the dark shadow of a microscopic plant seen in a thin slice of ancient chalcedony.

Sometimes these traces of life rest close to the surface—in a field where they may clang suddenly against the blade of a plow, in a sandy cliff quarried by waves, or in a hillside cut open by a bulldozer. Often, however, they are deep in the earth and may be seen only in a great gorge. And much of the record of life's past, it is known, lies undiscovered beneath the sea and the shore, buried in sediments and drowned when the land sank or the sea itself rose higher.

In the past few decades, scientists have acquired increasingly sophisticated tools, techniques and methods with which to interpret the scraps and remnants left by once-living things within the earth. They can now date the age of rock by using one of several radioactive clocks. By measuring the ratio of potassium to argon, or the decay of radioactive strontium and rubidium, for instance, they can fix the approximate age of a rock in the billions of years. By measuring the decay of carbon 14, they can give a much more precise reading within 50,000 years of the present. By determining the presence or absence of other carbon isotopes, they can decide—or make an educated guess—whether fossil tissue belonged to a plant or to an animal. There are elegant techniques now for making carbon replicas of microscopic fossils, for "shadowing" these replicas with metal and magnifying them hundreds of thousands of times with electron microscopes. (Some micro-fossils are so small that they are measured in fractions of a micron, a unit one millionth the length of a meter.) By identifying seeds or pollen grains, many of which persist for thousands of years in favorable circumstances, it is possible to reconstruct the flora and the climate that flourished when they grew. The kind of rock containing a fossil can, of course, suggest the kind of environment in which the plant or animal lived and died.

Today's paleontologists, archeologists and anthropologists, then, may not only be trained scientists but highly skilled detectives. The saga they are piecing together of life's prehistory, while incomplete, is often more fascinating, full of suspense, intrigue—and sometimes violence—than the best of Conan Doyle, Raymond Chandler, or Ian Fleming. Apparently, critical parts of the saga took place in the estuary over the ages.

It is hard for us who live only a few years to comprehend the concept of "geologic time"—the time since earth began. If, however, geologic time is compressed and considered in terms of a single calendar year, it is easier to gain some feeling for its scale. Suppose, then, that earth's year began at 12 a.m. on January 1st at the moment the planet commenced its spin around the sun; the present, of course, would be midnight of December 31st. According earth an age of something between four and a half and five billion years (the currently accepted guess), each month can then conveniently represent 400 million years. Each day would span about 13 million years,

In that world of sun and rock and water and patient moving sea, certain tides pulled down and left behind the shape of life, a gift of the universe, within the estuaries.

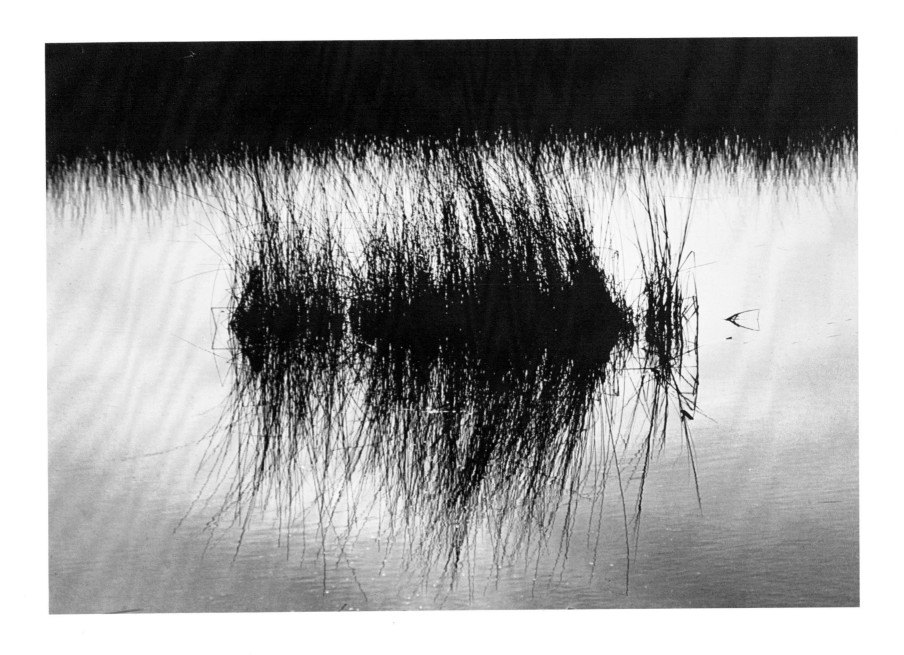

each hour more than half a million years, and each minute over 9 thousand years. The time it takes to read this page would encompass much of the history of *Homo sapiens sapiens,* or modern man.

Using this time scale, earth spun around the sun from that early January morning until the Ides of March, undergoing a lifeless but very real evolution. Around April first, the evolution became biological: life was born, perhaps in the estuary. Those first life forms, we surmise, were heterotrophic, unable to make their own food, needing and taking their nourishment from the environment around them. The estuary would have provided them with an optimum habitat for survival, offering the shelter of shallow waters and the nutritious broths of the river and the sea.

There followed a long period when those earliest life forms struggled to exist. Slowly, but inevitably, they exhausted the food supply around them until they were on the point of extinction. In ecologist Barry Commoner's words, they had "the fatal fault" of consuming their nonrenewable resources. But being able to change, and having the magic of adaptability, the early life forms invented a method of tapping the sun for energy. Using photosynthesis, they made their own food. Life became autotrophic, self-supporting, and off to a brave new start. Again in Commoner's words: "The first photosynthetic organisms transformed the rapacious, linear course of life into the earth's first great ecological cycle."..They closed the circle. It was an event almost as profoundly marvelous as genesis itself, for the way was opened for the evolution of new and increasingly complex life forms.

This extraordinary event occurred, we assume, some time around the middle of April in the earth's mythical year. For the next seven months — 2.8 billion years, more than half the time earth itself has existed — we have only tiny and intriguing hints of what life was, for life forms were microscopic in size. But, miraculously, there were encased in a few special rocks that persisted relatively undisturbed by geological accidents the incredibly small bodies of living plants that became microfossils billions of years ago.

Paleobotanist Elso S. Barghoorn has described three series of such microfossils which mark giant steps in life's continuing evolution. The earliest, found in rocks 3.2 billion years old, suggest that life was not only alive and well at that very ancient point in time—May 1st on our special calendar—but was photosynthetic as well. The second series, 2 billion years old, includes exquisitely organized blue-green algae; this provides evidence that life had become both terrestrial and diversified by August 1st. Barghoorn's most recent microfossils were found in billion-year-old rocks. Sophisticated green algae with well-organized cells, these fossils indicate that life had achieved much more diversity, much more complexity and, most importantly, the potential of sexual reproduction, in its next billion years of evolution. Intriguingly, each set of microfossils was found in chert which Barghoorn describes as "evidently the product of deposition in an aqueous environment rich in silica." He suggests further that this deposition occurred in shallow seas or embayments. Since silica is carried more abundantly in river water than in seawater, it seems reasonable to conjecture that these genesis plants may have lived in estuarine environments. The estuary would then have acted as a kind of paleontological museum, protecting and preserving in remarkable fashion the life forms that once flourished within it. More importantly, along with being a cradle for first life, the estuary may have been life's nursery as well.

We come now to the middle of October. The next 30 days of earth's mythical year apparently comprise one of the most extraordinary and puzzling periods in all of evolution. Amazing new relationships evidently developed between earth and the life it bore, and between plants and evolving animals. Perhaps the climate was especially benevolent, and the increasing oxygen being poured out by more and more plants may have sparked a profusion of new forms of life. When the known record resumes in mid-November, some 600 million years ago, it was suddenly a completely different world. Those Paleozoic seas were "swarming with highly differentiated plants and animals," as Barghoorn puts it. Life had assumed more complex forms. All the phyla of the invertebrate animals had evolved. Along with microscopic protozoa, curious soft-bodied creatures of many sizes and shapes —often with strange and beautiful appendages and tough shells and cases —moved in those warm waters and burrowed in the muddy sands and sandy muds along those primitive shores.

Some of those invertebrates, like the odd little trilobites, would fail to succeed and so become extinct, leaving only their intriguing fossils. Others, like certain brachiopods (animals which look like—but are not related to — the clams) would have the toughness, strength and ingenuity to persist and to become in our time living links with the past. Still others would give rise to ever more complex and successful creatures, to the first vertebrates, which appeared on the scene in the last week of November, and to their more sophisticated successors, which invaded and colonized the land some time during the first week of December.

The role the estuary played in this later evolution is debated in scientific circles. Some scientists agree that "adaptation to estuarine conditions preceded adaptation to fully freshwater conditions." In fact, Gordon Gunter, goes so far as to argue that "the vertebrates may have originated in shallow seas at lower salinities near the shore." Others believe the estuary had nothing to do with higher evolution.

It is surely no accident, nonetheless, that fossils of key evolutionary vertebrates have been found in low-lying deltaic sediments, where they lived in an area of lush vegetation with giant ferns towering over them, where slow streams meandered across the lowlands to empty into a great warm sea which lay nearby. Such a delta would provide an obvious bridge between the water and the land. And being a place of many ecological edges, it would open up many new niches to be exploited by the forms of life evolving within it.

In so rich an environment, the lobe-finned fishes, ancestors of man, mingled with other odd-looking animals that populated the waters and stream-banks. These animals left their bones in the muds of that ancient delta some 250 million years ago—near the middle of December. If one subscribes to Gunter's theory of vertebrate evolution, it would follow that they made their way inland from low-salinity coastal waters, adapting first to the world of the river and finally to the lake and to the land.

Like the trilobites, many of these early vertebrates became extinct as the weather changed and cruel cold and drought successively gripped their world. Some, however, survived—and may be found today still in the estuary. There is the lungfish, that odd "missing link," a creature half of the water and half of the land, able to breathe air, yet happy in the wet ooze of tropical lagoons. And there is the mudskipper which lives half in the water and half on the branches of mangroves that themselves grow with their roots in the warm waters of tropical estuaries.

Other species which have survived even longer in evolutionary time occupy today's estuary. There are numerous estuarine tunicates—soft-bodied creatures which were among the first animals to have embedded in them the semblance of a backbone. And one of the brachiopods, described as "almost a facsimile of the oldest living genus in the world," lives (or did, before the area was drenched with polluted waters) in southern California tidal flats, fastening its curious stalk into the wet and muddy sands, feeding on the rich organic matter washed over it.

In the plant world, a green alga grows in profusion on the great delta of the Ganges, among other places. This small hardy plant is able to tolerate great periods of dessication and to survive, even as those successful early vertebrates of the delta did. Its cells are organized in what appears to be a crude root system, a stem and a leafy portion. From such a plant, the more complex terrestrial green plants may have evolved—the liverworts, the mosses, and later, the ferns that crept onto the land

If one subscribes to the theory that the individual development of an animal recapitulates the evolutionary development of its species, there are other curious links to the estuary. As we know, many fish and shellfish require the estuary for crucial periods of growth in their lives—suggesting that they spent evolutionary time in this place. Many oysters require estuarine conditions to spawn, and the microscopic spat have within them an innate directive to migrate upstream into riverine waters to avoid being washed out to sea and destroyed. There is further the inborn ability of many higher fishes to adapt to estuarine conditions, prompting the thought that they may in their past history have occupied less salty waters than the sea.

Finally there is the curious fact that evolution is occurring actively in the estuary even today. The grass shrimp, for example, are found now in three different habitats—marine, estuarine and freshwater—in three different evolutionary forms. As biologist Joel Hedgpeth notes, they appear to be in "process of migration from the sea." And Hedgpeth describes the "terrestrial tendencies of a marine gastropod (or snail) which is found in abundance in estuaries as well as on higher ground." Indeed, one species of fiddler crab in Japan is scuttling around at elevations of over 2,000 feet.

I sometimes think of the role of the estuary in life's evolution when I finger the lovely spiral shell of a moon snail, or when I hear the lonely evening cry of a night heron, descendant of birds which have flown untold millions of years. Or when I watch the sun light up the channels of Bolinas Lagoon as they wind across the wet mud flats to encounter the pulsing tide. This is an elemental place, embodying basic and stubborn forces of the earth and of life itself. If we fail to understand such a place, to respect it and to care for it—if we continue to destroy it as we continue to destroy other parts of our home, the earth—we may well be cutting ourselves off from the point of many of life's beginnings. More sadly, we may be denying important beginnings still meant to come.

7. Man in the estuary

Along the west coast, winter is the rainy season. We can expect a whole procession of storms starting in November. Some are gentle, trailing soft showers easily across the land. Others are the wild cyclonic ones that drench the earth with torrents of rain, flood out the roads, and lash the trees along the shore until they grow prostrate, assuming the shape of the land they lean against. Despite these hard storms, the season is mild enough, and life in the estuary is spared the fierce changes of temperature that occur further north.

Spring does not make a grand entrance here. Instead it slips in easily and early, insinuating delicious days—all balmy and golden—between the heaviest storms. (The coming of spring is more a state of mind than a happening here, says a friend of my oldest daughter, a young woman used to Maine weather.) By March, the storms are tapering off and new life is unfolding. The slopes of the mountain are soaked, their grasses spread out like green velvet beneath the fresh skies. Rivulets run in the creases of the hills. The canyons echo to the steady pounding of swollen white-water streams. In the marshes, the fresh water slips buoyantly over the brine. The small river that empties into Bolinas Lagoon flows high and swift, cutting new channels across the delta at its mouth. Alders hang out their tasselled catkins and lupines come in bloom, splashing the hills with streaks and washes of blue. The days grow longer. The buds of the buckeye burst, uncurling gold-green scimitars of leaves. Wild lilacs perfume the air. There is a steady gentle hum of bees.

A feeling stirs early among the birds that have wintered here. *Zugunruhe*, the Germans call it. It is a kind of restlessness as they sense deep within them an old need awakening, the need to move, to fly to far places, to make new life. The wintering flocks begin to leave. Caught up like leaves in a whirlwind, they spiral into the sky, swoop and circle, then settle out in strong steady flights northward.

Up the small river above the marsh one day come the first of the silver salmon, splashing through the shallows, wriggling among the shadows, then resting, becoming long sinuous shadows themselves. I marvel at them, compelled as they are to bring their lives full circle, to find their place of birth to spawn, and then to die. Having known the wide wild freedom of the sea, they have returned unerringly to this place, remembering, it is said, the old familiar smells of home.

Salmon may use the stars to plot their courses even as certain birds do. Indeed, I think of the salmon and other fish, the shad and alewives, mackeral and herring, the sturgeon and the striped bass, as birds of the sea. They have their *Zugunruhe* and their flyways, too. They travel together in flocks, moving in concert to elemental rhythms. They help to circulate earth's nutrients, carrying them into many parts of the sea's waters, and inland when they migrate up the rivers of the continents.

Man has long taken fish from the estuaries of the planet, even as he has taken the shellfish, the wildfowl and shorebirds. Being a tough animal himself, and the most ingenious and adaptable of all, it is likely that he learned how to get along in the estuary, and put it to his use early in his history—perhaps when he first saw the salmon run.

Although we like to consider the earth our private property, the family of man has occupied it an exceedingly brief period in terms of geological time. The first mammals did not evolve until mid-December of earth's mythical year, and the primates, more immediate progenitors of man, did not develop until the early afternoon of December 26th. There are several estimates of the advent of the hominids, our closer ancestors, but if we take fifteen million years ago as a conservative date, these creatures came on the scene shortly before midnight of December 30th. And man himself appeared about 10 p.m. on New Years Eve. He sowed his first seeds a shade before 11:59 p.m., and the Christian era commenced just a few seconds before the bells would signal midnight.

The record of our brief time on earth is, like that of so much of the life that preceded us, far from complete. Of the past thirty to forty thousand years we do have enough evidence to put together a fairly consecutive history. But of man's earlier years, of his beginnings, and of his slow evolution into the genus, *Homo*, the traces are fewer. The events of one period, from four to eleven million years ago, are almost wholly unknown. Human tissue does not persist long after death, and human bone requires rather special conditions if it is to last more than a few decades. Where the climate has been generally temperate and dry during the millennia, where the earth has formed troughs and basins and sealed away their contents relatively undisturbed—as with the sifting down of tuff or pumice—a few of man's and pre-man's bones have been preserved. Along the great rift of Africa, for instance, and in parts of India and China, some very ancient finds have been made—sometimes only a piece of jaw or the bones of a hand or a foot, but enough to suggest reconstruction of the individual to whom they once belonged. From this fragmentary fossil evidence, the dim sequence of man's evolution has been put together. Though new biochemical methods of relating man's evolution to that of his closest relatives, the apes, are being developed, they are largely unproved; most anthropologists still prefer to base their more important speculations on the fossil record.

Since new finds and evidence are continuously being uncovered, such speculations must necessarily undergo continuous revision. Ideas accepted just a few years ago, for instance, may now be obsolete, and some hypotheses are out of date by the time they are properly published. One theory about man's evolution was based rather rigidly on what turned out to be a monumental hoax—the Piltdown skull—much to the chagrin of a few learned men.

The principles of evolution are more certain—or, at least, more broadly accepted. It is generally agreed, for instance, that the environment in which a species evolves plays a major part in its evolution, and vice versa; that is, there is constant interaction between life forms and their environment, and the two continuously affect one another. The same principle applies to the interaction between life forms themselves. Competition for food or space or shelter can be a dominant evolutionary agent, with natural selection acting to determine which species and which individuals will succeed. Man, like all animals, has been and is subject to these evolutionary laws.

The current belief is that man shares with the apes a common "prosimian," or early primate, ancestor which gave rise to the higher primates. At some uncertain date (an educated guess says thirty-five million years ago), the higher primates diverged in their evolutionary pathways. One path led to the New World monkeys; the other to the Old World monkeys. Some time between fifteen and twenty million years ago, the Old World monkeys split again. The pongids (or great apes) continued their trek in the forest world; the hominids (man's forefathers) began to live on the forest edge and to move more and more into the open country, finding and exploiting new habitats. As the hominids adapted to their new surroundings, they developed characteristics which distinguished them from the pongids and other monkeys.

Perhaps because they can be documented more or less in the fossil record, certain of these characteristics—the dental apparatus, the postcranial skeleton, and of most importance, the size of the skull, the bony case of the brain—are used as indicators by anthropologists as they chart the increasing "human-ness" of the evolving hominids, and their divergence from the pongids. Differences in dentition—in the size, kind and arrangement of the teeth—reflected emerging differences in feeding habits. Skeletal differences reflected the hominid's increasingly upright posture, his bipedal locomotion which culminated in his striding walk, his shorter prehensile arms, and his exquisitely articulated hands with their precision-gripping and power-gripping ability. An ever larger brain capacity allowed the hominid—and then the man—to develop more sophisticated systems of intra-communication resulting in language, and to devise and use with skill increasingly complex and efficient tools. In contrast, the apes evolved a set of physical and mental equipment which fitted them more and more to live successfully if exclusively in their forest environment.

The evolution of certain other striking features of man is undocumented simply because these features involve the soft tissues and therefore left no convenient fossil record. Thus it is not known at what point in time— or how or why—man became less hairy, acquired a highly developed system of sweat glands, a subcutaneous layer of fat, a more prominent nose, or why the two sexes became so pronouncedly bimorphic, or the human female evolved her particular curvature and her permanently enlarged adult breast which, in itself, distinguishes her from the other female primates. Any explanation of these characteristics is necessarily based on surmise; anthropologists generally do not use these human features as indicators in considering man's evolution.

According to one school of thought, it is possible for major evolutionary changes to occur in a matter of ten thousand years or so, but most such changes take a great deal longer to become established in the gene pool of a species. Apparently, man took his time in evolving and gradually acquired his human qualities through all the hours of the last day of earth's mythical year. He may have first left the forest world because he was forced out, perhaps by reason of competition with his pongid cousins, or perhaps because of climatic or geological change. He may, on the other hand, have chanced into the more open woodland at forest's edge and chosen to live along the waterways or around the lakes he found there, or beside a seacoast. At any rate, his success in exploiting new habitats increasingly changed his social ways as well as his physical characteristics. At some point in the last few million years, he became an adept hunter of other animals. He invented effective instruments for killing, and for preparing his food. The hunting society, moreover, promoted increasingly cooperative behavior among its members as well as a distinct division of labor between the sexes.

As hunters (and fishermen, for they were both) early men had relatively little impact on their environment, although they took their toll of other species. They were few in number, nomadic, and lived, as certain peoples still do, close to the earth. During the past few millennia, however, *Homo* became an extraordinarily successful genus. He came to dominate and modify his habitat more and more. And when modern man first dug into the land and turned it over to plant seeds, he initiated an era of environmental change that would grow progressively rapid, complex and profound. Now civilized man controls the farthest reaches of the earth and the fate of all the life that the earth supports.

In exceedingly simplified outline, this is a sketch of man's evolutionary history as it is presently conceived. Yet even when the story is fleshed out with details based on known fossil evidence, much of it remains speculative. The fossil evidence is meager, and there are big bothersome gaps of time still to be accounted for. There are also some curious human characteristics which are not explained, but which must be fitted into the puzzle.

Take, for instance, the matter of man's hairlessness, or more accurately, his reduced hairiness. Whether or not this is a major differentiating feature between man and his related primates, it is obviously an interesting one. And when six distinguished scientists speculate on the reason for it, they come up, typically, with six different hypotheses. Thus, one postulates that man shed his hair as a nonessential feature once he had invented clothing to keep himself warm. Another argues that hair loss was a mechanism (associated with an increased number of sweat glands) which man the hunter adapted to help dissipate the heat accompanying exertion, particularly in a warm climate. A third scientist thinks that man's—and woman's—body-hair patterns are "almost certainly the result of sexual selection." A fourth explains that the metabolic energy used by man's body to produce and maintain hair "proved more useful to man's survival when channelled into the production of other characteristics," and so was selected "out." The fifth says that "patterns of hairiness in man may follow evolutionary changes in diet or other factors." And the sixth suggests that man lost his hair because nakedness helped him avoid the body insects—such as disease-carrying lice and ticks—which plague so many of his furry friends.

Still another noted scientist has a different explanation. Sir Alister Hardy, the British zoologist, proposes that man lost his hair during a time in his pre-history when he lived as much in the water as he did on land. In an article entitled "Was Man More Aquatic In The Past?," Hardy suggests that man spent a crucial evolutionary period in a coastal environment. The influence of this habitat, he explains, accounts not only for man's comparative hairlessness but for several other of his important distinguishing features.

Hardy notes that certain prehistoric animals which at one time lived on land were forced back into the sea at a later date by "overpopulation and shortages of food." Turtles, water snakes, dolphins, porpoises, whales and penguins, among other animals, all readapted to marine life successfully. Pre-man, Hardy postulates, if he shared the fate of these other creatures, may have been crowded out of his forest world. Naturally, he turned to the nearest shallow and warm coastal waters for the food so readily available there. Presumably, he chose an estuarine area to remain close to a source of fresh water.

Hardy envisions man as still being dependent on both arms and legs to get around—a knuckle-walker, in fact—when he was forced to make this major change in habitat. This allowed him to keep his balance easily as he moved into the water and felt around the bottom of those ancient bays for clams and sea urchins and other edibles. Plucking, clutching, and prizing out his prey developed new suppleness, sensitivity and skillfulness in his hands. At the same time, the need to crack open shellfish prompted this early man to use the stones he found around him and so his earliest tool-making was fostered.

First wading on all fours, man gradually learned to "toddle," and perhaps to swim. When he ventured into deeper waters, he found he could stand, resting his feet on the bottom with his head above the water. With his body held erect, his hands were free to be used in eating the food he had gathered nearer the shore. But, more importantly, having once learned to balance himself upright, he would soon try out this new posture back on the land.

To bolster his thesis, Hardy notes that man still has an innate affinity for the water. (Infants, indeed, can be taught to swim before they can learn to walk.) There is the universal popularity of the seashore and man's enthusiasm for swimming and surfing as further evidence. There is also the subcutaneous layer of fat which gives both human sexes a graceful stream-lined shape. No other primate has this fat layer, yet it is common among such forms of aquatic life as the porpoises, the dolphins and the whales.

First wading on all fours, man gradually learned to "toddle," and perhaps to swim. When he ventured into deeper waters, he found he could stand, resting his feet on the bottom with his head above the water. Having once learned to balance himself upright, he would soon try out this new posture back on the land.

And there is man's hairlessness. Hardy observes that "loss of hair is characteristic of a number of aquatic animals." Hair retards speed in the water, as Hardy points out, to the extent that members of crack swimming teams shave off all their body hair before racing. There is another interesting bit of evidence: hair tracts on the human foetus lie as though shaped by the streams of water that pass around a swimmer as he moves face-down, as in the classic Australian crawl. Hardy believes that man retained the hair on his head for protection, a point on which other scientists agree. And he estimates the period of man's stay in the estuaries or shallow coastal areas at some time between five and fifteen million years ago. (This would embrace one of those provocative pre-history gaps mentioned earlier.)

Another scientist, who has done pioneer work in Georgia's estuaries, has independently developed a line of thinking much like Hardy's. Botanist Philip F.-C. Greear places man right in the salt marshes at a critical, if intermediate, stage of his evolution, perhaps at a date somewhat later than that proposed by Hardy. Greear suggests that man was forced out of the forest by a harsh change in climate. In a period of heavy glaciation, ice sheets covered the land and crowded man ever closer to the shore. In the higher latitudes, he probably perished from the cold. Closer to the equator, Greear suggests, he may have found a good home in the marshes and estuarine areas where there was fresh water handy, a rich and ready food supply, and the protection of tall grasses.

Like Hardy, Greear believes that the marsh environment accounted for many human characteristics: for man's upright posture, his beautifully designed hands, his subcutaneous layer of fat, his lasting affinity for water, and, of course, his hairlessness. Greear notes further that a diet of shellfish would have fostered the evolution of man's unique dental apparatus: grinding molars are good tools for reducing shellfish to particles of a digestible size. He points out also that man's prominent nose with protected nostrils—very different from the nose of other primates—could well have evolved as man learned to swim face-down in the water. A paddle-shaped foot, particularly noticeable among some of the world's best natural swimmers, such as the sleek-bodied people of the Barbados, would also be selected for in a swimming primate.

As both Hardy and Greear are quick to admit, the "aquatic theory" is pure speculation. There is no fossil evidence to back it up. Yet both men use this fact as an argument in their favor. They point out that there is probably a good deal of unexplored fossil evidence in earth's coastal regions, silted over, buried, and drowned as the sea rose some 300 feet after the last ice age. If man had been a coastal dweller as they propose, he would of course have left his relics in the particular region of the shore which is now under water. This would help explain some of the great blanks in man's evolutionary history.

While most anthropologists question the aquatic theory, there is no question that the estuary has been quite important to man in more recent times. Fossil evidence of coastal cultures along the southern shores of the Mediterranean, in fact, dates back at least a half a million years. Shell mounds that go back many millennia are found at the mouths of rivers throughout the world. More recent man left his kitchen middens on every continent

A feeling stirs early among the birds. **Zugunruhe,** the Germans call it. It is a kind of restlessness as they sense deep within them an old need awakening, the need to move, to fly to far places, to make new life.

—in Denmark, Scotland, Japan, the Aleutian Islands, and in many places along the coasts of the Americas there are piles of broken shells to tell of the early fishermen who were there. Certain Mesolithic cultures evidently survived times of great cold only by living off the shellfish and fish in their coastal waters. Some middens were built up in layers, indicating that people used these sites repeatedly, sometimes for thousands of years. Many were in continuous use long before man planted grain.

Shell mounds have yielded some important archeological finds. From certain early ones have come flakes, axes, awls, and weights for holding fishing nets. From later mounds have come clues to man's developing culture, his use of certain shells for sophisticated ornaments and for money. Some early tribes, in fact, developed complex cultures supported by a coastal-based economy. And entire civilizations—such as the classic one cradled by the Nile delta—grew up in estuarine regions.

At some early time in his use of the estuary, man invented the fish weir, an ingenious device to trap fish. A fish weir is a simple structure, but it demands of its builder a kind of native engineering skill and a degree of art. Designed in many different shapes and sizes, the weir is basically a fence or wall set up across the mouth of a river, placed to take advantage of the tides in the estuary. It may be a row of stakes laced through with "wattles" of brush, or stakes, or brush alone. Usually, a "leader" or angled section of the wall deflects the running fish on flood tide, forcing them into a pocket where they are caught and held when the water ebbs. It is easy enough then to harvest the fish with nets, or seines, arrows or spears.

There are relics of weirs on all the continents, and weirs continue in active use today in certain places in Africa and Asia. (Marine biologists deplore them, since they can now wipe out whole populations of fish.) One particular weir is of special interest to us. It was placed in a Massachusetts estuary about 5,000 years ago by a tribe of unknown people who discovered there a bounty of fish and shellfish. Around the estuary were low hills covered with oak and sassafras and sweet-smelling pine. The people built villages there, or so we think, but no trace has been found of the kitchen middens they must have left, no charred bones or charcoal, no remnant of their dwellings. But we know that many prehistoric men occupied the estuary of the river we call the Charles because they built an extraordinary structure there, a complicated fish weir of great size.

The stakes of the weir were buried under several feet of sediment and water for thousands of years before the English sailed into Boston Harbor. They were buried deeper after the city of Boston was built and the bay was filled repeatedly to make new land. They were discovered by chance not long ago by workmen excavating for subways and skyscrapers. These men found a puzzling thing—wood where no wood was meant to be, a great array of stakes and wattles. Well preserved in silt and mud and sand, the structure was clearly the work of earlier men, and too bizarre to go unremarked.

A group of scientists collaborated to solve the puzzle—or, at least parts of it. The scientists were familiar with sediments and shells, with trees and other plants, with pollen grains, diatoms and forams. They measured the stakes, plotted the way they were placed, sectioned the wood and studied its structure under microscopes. Knowing the pattern of cells in certain trees and the way spring growth lays down new wood, they could figure the kind of trees from which the stakes and wattles had been cut, and the time of year of the cutting. They sifted the silt and probed layers of peat, picking out the cases of diatoms, the grains of pollen, the tiny shells of forams, pieces of plants, larger shells, and even the feather of a bird. Identifying the species of all these various relics, they could calculate the climate when they prospered, and how salty the water was they stood or grew in, and what kind of marshes and bottom land the stakes were driven into.

When they were finished putting together the myriad bits of evidence entombed for so long in the bed of the Charles' estuary, they concluded that a large and thriving colony of prehistoric fishermen once lived where Boston now stands, at a time when there were forests and tidal flats and marshes much like today's. The picture of those early men is more vague. All that is clear is that they placed tens of thousands of stakes in the estuary, in an order not fully understood, since the margins of that early weir were not uncovered. But they built great walls—row after parallel row—and they must have worked in large crowds to set up so large a structure.

We know that they cut the stakes in early spring, when the ice was finally out of the river and April's warmer showers were melting away the last rinds of old winter snow. We can imagine them stooping to take the supple young saplings of beech and oak and sassafras, using sharpened stones, and then sitting along the banks of the estuary, their strong hands working the pungent wood with rough tools, stripping away the small branches from the stakes and painstakingly sharpening the ends that would be driven into the silt. These early fishermen saw the shad begin to run, and the shadbush shake out its white blossoms on the tips of its branches. And as the weeks progressed, their woods were starred with the pale blossoms of dogwood even as New England woods are today.

They must have set their stakes while the river still ran cold. Bracing against the heavy spring waters, the melt-off of ice and snow, they drove the saplings into the silt and the peat of their salt marshes, where grew the same grasses and reeds and rushes that still grow in many eastern marshes. Finally they pushed down the leafy branches of bayberry and hickory, beech and alder for their wattles. They were done by mid-June, and their weir was ready.

They took their fish when the river had quieted down, and as the tides provided. When summer came, they took oysters, too. In fact, some argue that these early men were oystermen, and that they built their weir to catch the oyster spat. If so, they chose the right spot near the river's mouth, and put out their stakes at the right time of year, ready for the young to settle out as the waters warmed with summer. At any rate, they had enormous beds of oysters growing on the wattles, the shellfish so thickly crowded that some took the shape of long narrow "cat's tongues." The people must have gathered many, and left the rest in the estuary to be harvested later.

For many springs, those early fishermen were there in the estuary, repairing their weir, replacing stakes knocked down by the winter's ice, rebuilding sections washed out or buried. Silting was a big problem. The waters of the estuary ran heavy with sediment, and the stakes and wattles themselves helped to trap and hold the clays and sands. But the men were not easily discouraged and, perhaps like later New Englanders, they were loathe to change their ways. They laid down layer after layer of wattles, and drove thousands of stakes year after year.

One unknown year they stopped. There may have been a massive storm that winter that changed their estuary radically. Perhaps it buried their oyster beds, or the wash of sand and clay was too much for the weirmen to cope with. They left as they came, without a trace, moving on down the coast looking for an easier place to live, or returning to an earlier home. Those early people were the ancestors, perhaps, of the Indians whom the white men found when they came to the new world.

The story of this fish weir is instructive, not simply because men built a weir in an estuary nearly five thousand years ago, but because that weir was found beneath twenty-six feet of sediment, sealed away under the bottom of Boston Bay. It might well have gone forever undetected but for the chance excavation of its site. This raises the possibility, of course, that Hardy and Greear are right after all. How many other fish weirs lie hidden under the sea? How many middens? How many artifacts and relics of man's more ancient past rest under straits and shallows, buried beneath bays and harbors —or even under deeper waters? Until far more paleontologic work is done in offshore areas, the tantalizing questions remain unanswered.

It is perhaps no great coincidence that the Puritans chose the estuary of the Charles—which they called Boston Harbor—when they arrived in the new world more than four thousand years after our early weirmen were there. It was a good place to settle and build a town. William Wood wrote of Boston in 1634: "His situation is very pleasant, being a Peninsula hem'd in on the South-side by the Bay of Roxberry, on the North-side with Charles-river, the Marshes on the back side being not halfe a quarter mile over: so that a little fencing will secure their cattle from the Woolues." True, in spring the waters swelled so deep on high tides that horses went in above their knees crossing the Neck, the narrow ribbon of land that ran across the marshes connecting Boston to the mainland. But soon, Wood recorded, the enterprising colonists had "built a Wayre to catch Fish, wherein they take great store of Shad and Alewives. In two Tydes they have gotten one hundred thousand of those fishes: This is no smalle benefit to the plantation." And since they also found oyster reefs (soon exhausted) in Boston Bay, they ate well in those early days, "Woolues" notwithstanding.

The settlers who followed also took advantage of the estuaries that lay along the eastern seaboard. The way the coast was shaped influenced profoundly the course of their history. The settlers found shelter in estuaries, safe harbor for their ships, and gateways inland up the great rivers that flowed into the Atlantic Ocean, one after another, from Maine to Florida. The colonists located their first cities—Boston, Providence, New York, Baltimore, Charleston — on the shores of estuaries, taking fresh water from the rivers, and feasting as earlier men had done before them on the bounty of seafood they found waiting for them. Indeed, as one astute observer has noted, their great success in the New World was "due in no small part to the rich, easily harvested resources of the estuaries."

But those first white settlers were not content, as most red men had been before them, to live gently and in harmony with the land. They had to subdue it. They took the seafood resource and used it as a base for their economic ventures—and they took the fur-bearing animals of the estuary, too. They cut the trees along the shores and up the rivers, put out cattle to graze the salt marshes, filled the soft tidal flats to make new land. They built piers and wharves and warehouses along the shores of the bays and harbors, which soon became centers for their growing commerce. They concentrated their increasing populations quite naturally around the estuaries, dumped their human waste into them and piled their garbage on the marshes. They had no idea that the rich coastal regions were among their most important natural resources, or that they were initiating a pattern of use that could eventually destroy them.

Today, a vast megalopolis sprawls over hundreds of square miles of estuarine lands—almost continuously along the eastern seaboard, around the Gulf of Mexico, and increasingly around our west coast estuaries. Although coastal regions account for only 15 per cent of the total land area of the United States, a third of the American people are now jammed into them, along with 40 per cent of the nation's industry. Paper and cotton mills, chemical and petroleum plants, steel refineries, atomic reactors, docks, airports, warehouses all crowd the shores of our harbors, bays and other estuarine areas—and sewage outfalls gush between them. Pollution generated around estuaries, in fact, is staggering. In 1969, for example, more than eight billion gallons of municipal wastes and twenty-two billion gallons of manufacturing wastes were discharged daily into the estuarine waters of America. About half of the human sewage and two-thirds of the industrial wastes were totally untreated. Added to this was the oil and waste from tankers, freighters, naval vessels, pleasure boats and other vessels. Compounding such pollution of estuaries are the dams upstream that reduce the flow of fresh water, nutrients, and silt deposition. And dredging, filling, diking, and mining of sand, gravel, sulfur, petroleum, phosphate, and sometimes oyster shells—all contribute to the estuary's deterioration. So does the heated water discharged by some factories—and by all atomic facilities.

We have not yet framed effective laws to control man's use of the estuary. Efforts of federal and local governments in this direction are still in the beginning stages. Without such laws, the abuse continues—often unheeded and unchecked until it is too late, and the damage is irrevocable. Yet it is clearly in our interest to stop destroying and to start understanding our estuaries. They are vital places not only to the plants and animals which inhabit them. Estuaries in good working order are essential to the proper functioning of earth's life support system as we know it. Which means, of course, that they are essential to the survival of man.

Part III:
The life and times
of a West Coast estuary

8. Bolinas Lagoon

Twilight is a time of enchantment in Bolinas Lagoon. The sunsets here are often vividly colored, with sheaves of clouds stained yellow and crimson and coral, and strips of pale green sky banded between them. The evening light has a special quality. It slants in horizontally, silhouetting the sand spit and the mesa and making black shadows of them, pouring over the soft folds of the mountain in a radiant flood. A thin gauze of mist adds luster to the air. The waters of the estuary lie quiet and glossy, reflecting the skies, taking on the shades and shapes of the clouds, glowing as though lit from within. Even the faintest wind trails a dark shadow over such a smooth surface. The mountain holds the light until the very end, turning gold and rose and mauve, and then black when the full tide of darkness wells up from the water. The lights of the distant city shine out then in a thick strand on the southern horizon, glittering like gems.

Most of the shorebirds leave the island and the marshes at night, some moving offshore to the nearby reef, some into the meadows. They start up in gyres of flight, their underbodies flashing like a shake of white petals against the darkening sky. Geese often choose this time to travel. It is hard to see the long clean shape of their dark bodies then, but the whistle of their wings can sometimes be heard. The dabbling ducks linger close to shore. They paddle along with their heads completely underwater, appearing decapitated; or they stand on end for long moments, their forked tails sticking up in crazy patterns. Often they come up on the land to sleep, and an early morning traveler may surprise them slumbering beside the road.

I like to walk along the shore near the channel in the early darkness of a summer night. I come upon the startling white shape of a snowy egret. I listen to the night herons cry out to one another as they leave the cypress trees. The water makes a long slow hiss as it drains to the sea.

I watch the lamps go on in the houses along the shore and spill out their light onto the water. Somebody sings; a phone clangs; there is a sudden blare of canned music, and I see through a curtained window the blue glow of a television screen. A glare of headlights stabs the night, and a car crowds me to the side of the road. The egret remains motionless, used to the presence of people here.

I think of the earlier people who lived more quietly along these shores, those whose bare feet marked out the first trails across the mountain. They were few in number and they lived closely with the earth, knowing it intimately, its rocks and trees, its streams and shores. They named themselves for the land or the water; a boy-baby—a "new person" to them—might be called "salmon-going-down-creek-in-water." They placed shell beads on their dead and believed their spirits returned to the sea. They had a feeling for their fellow creatures, especially for the birds. They used the feathers of pelicans and condors for their ceremonies, and knew that there had been a race of birds before there was a race of men.

I wonder what these Indians thought when they first saw the white man's sails gleaming against the western sky, and the thrust of the ship's prow into the estuary. They could not have guessed the portent of that arrival. They were guileless people. They crowned a king among the first comers, so the story goes. But that was before the strangers took their land, and then their lives.

The summer nights are often warm here, but sometimes I shiver when I turn from the shore with its bright lights and its loud noises, and climb the hill toward home.

The estuary we now call Bolinas Lagoon was formed, as were all of the present coasts, by the rise of the sea following the last great ice age. It is a classic tectonic land form, being the drowned southern end of the narrow rift valley formed by the San Andreas Fault, one of the most spectacular and active earthquake faults on earth. Here, a few miles north of San Francisco, it cuts in from the sea and runs between high steep escarpments for nearly twelve miles. The fault separates two distinct land masses.

To the west of the fault lies Point Reyes Peninsula, a triangular piece of land which juts into the Pacific ocean, its apex curving in a hook to form Drake's Bay. Although it is called a peninsula, and nestles close to the land mass to the east, it is, in effect, a geological "island" which has been dragged northwest along the fault line at an average rate of about ½ inch a year during the past several million years. It is composed in part of ancient granite (found nowhere east of the San Andreas Fault, although it crops up suggestively in places far to the south and to the north of here), but predominately of mudstone and shale several million years old. Near the estuary, there are more recent, loosely consolidated marine and estuarine siltstones and sandstones overlying the deeper deposits. The southern end of the peninsula consists of a broad pleateau lying about 200 feet above the sea and sloping gently northward to a spine of hills, Inverness Ridge. Considered a fine example of a marine terrace, this plateau or mesa forms the western shore of the estuary.

The mountain ridge to the east of the rift valley is a spur of Mt. Tamalpais, rising in the California Coast Range. Called Bolinas Ridge, it is composed of rocks and soils belonging to the Franciscan group, a jumble of sediments—graywacke sandstone, chert, shale, serpentine, and pillow basalts —which were gathered originally in a deep offshore trench in Jurassic times, perhaps 130 million years ago. Mt. Tamalpais is not overlain by any younger sediments here, and is believed to be part of an ancient high upland which has remained above the sea for untold millennia. It is well worn, although steep canyons are incised in it. Its soil is thin in many places and almost uniformly very crumbly. The rocks along the fault line, already rubble, have probably been fragmented further and ground even finer by the movements of the earth. They form a loosely compacted friable soil described as a *melange.*

The land of the rift valley itself is a mixture of rocks from the peninsula and the mountain, poorly consolidated, crushed and sheared by fault movements. It is laced through with many ancillary fault lines, so that sag ponds and trenches are common features of the landscape.

The freshwater drainage of these unique watersheds is arranged curiously, due in part to the active faulting. The small river that runs year round into the estuary has its headwaters in a spring on Inverness Ridge. Halfway along its course it picks up waters from the high mountain ridge on the east, thus draining both land masses as well as the southern part of the rift valley.

Other canyons of the mountain's ridge drain directly into the estuary, with a dozen streams flowing in year-round. The freshwater input here varies greatly with the seasons: in winter it is plentiful from heavy rains; in the dry summers, it diminishes greatly. The streams in the canyons, although perennial, sometimes slow to mere trickles by August or September, but the small river delivers sweet water continuously.

Fogs often add their moisture here. Lying offshore for days, a sea of fog may sweep in on a hot day and lap against the toe of the mountain, then curl back like a giant wave. Oddly enough, the fog may part above the estuary and let the sun through while it swathes the mesa and the lower part of the mountain.

Bolinas Lagoon has been subject to extremes of geological change and impact. Being part of an active earthquake fault, its basin has been repeatedly shaken and fractured as the earth has moved. In addition, the soils of the lands that cradle it are unusually susceptible to erosion; unless pegged down by trees and plants they disintegrate readily. The cliffs of the mesa along the shore are loose and easily washed away. The ocean quarries them constantly and offshore currents sweep in a heavy load of their sand. Part of this sand burden forms the beautifully curved sand spit here; part builds up the island inside the mouth of the estuary; the rest goes to fill the estuary's basin. More than half the sediments in the basin have washed down from the inland watersheds, especially during heavy winter storms. As the load builds up, the scouring action of the currents in the estuary is modified, the waters become more shallow, and the bar across the mouth grows higher. Eventually the basin will become a coastal marsh, and finally a meadow, barring drastic movement along the fault line or a change in sea level.

The climate here has swung through as many changes as the land. When it was cool, trees and plants moved down from northerly regions; when warm, they invaded from the south. Remnants of the different flora remained, most spectacularly the redwoods, *Sequoia sempervirens,* the tallest

The evening light has a special quality. It slants in horizontally, silhouetting the sand spit and the mesa and making black shadows of them, pouring over the soft folds of the mountain in a radiant flood.

living things on earth. Their seeds probably found the canyons of the mountain several million years ago and took root to form part of the magnificent forest that is making its last stand along the rim of the north California coast. The redwoods and other conifers such as Douglas fir came from the north at a time of temperate climate and summer rains. They succeeded in staying when the climate grew drier and winter became the rainy season because their needles could condense the fog to form a measurable "drip," which may add several inches to the annual rainfall. Now they stand next to trees and flowers that moved in from the south — the coastal oaks, the madrone, the manzanita and other shrubs of the chaparral that thrive in warm, dry open country which they find here on sheltered eastern slopes.

It must have been a paradise that the first men found when they came here a few thousand years ago. In the canyons and on the ridge towered the tall straight columns of the redwoods, with a lacy understory of hazel and tanbark oak, and delicate ferns and vines and ladyslipper orchids at their feet. On the slopes of the ridge sprawled oak and laurel, flattened by the offshore winds. Douglas fir and pine made deeper forests in the more protected places. Buckeye, alder and willow shaded the lower, wetter canyons along the streams.

Eelgrass likely streamed in the estuary's waters, making an aquatic forest home for the moon snails and sea snails. At certain seasons, the sky darkened with black brant, the geese that require this sea grass for their food. Grizzly bears scooped salmon from the small river and black bears and wolverine roamed the woods. Mountain lions thinned the herds of deer and elk that fed in the rift valley. Coyotes and coastal wolves made wild music in the evenings. Fur seals and sea otters found protection along the shores. And condors spread their dark magnificent wings and rode the thermals above the valley.

The first known men to leave their traces here were members of the Miwok tribe, coastal Indians who depended on the bounty of the sea for their food and way of life. Coming and going like the black brant when the seasons changed, they camped in many parts of the peninsula and the valley, especially along the streams when the fishing and hunting were at their best.

They had both fear and respect for the earthquakes that shook the land. They thought they were caused by the restless stirrings of a giant who lay sleeping face down beneath the ground with his arms outstretched. When the giant moved his fingers, the earth trembled above him. They gave the earthquake-maker shell money, and beads, thrown into a big fire, to placate him and keep him quiet.

The Coast Miwok shared the land ethic of many other Indians of their time. They did not consider that they owned the land. It was simply their home. The different tribes, distinguished as much by language as anything else, defined their own territories by prominent features of the landscape, such as high ridges. Inside the territories, the use of certain hunting areas and fishing spots along the streams and shores belonged to members of the tribe. Though no Miwok laid claim to this land, a man or woman could own a tree and mark its bark to show his ownership. One might own a buckeye and take its sticks which were so good for fire-making. Another might

Buckeye, alder and willow shaded the lower, wetter canyons. Grass streamed in the estuary's waters, making an aquatic forest home for the moon snails and sea snails.

own an oak for its acorns, or a manzanita for its berries, or a laurel for its spicy leaves, which made a healing tea. They did not log their trees and never sold them, but considered them part of a family's heritage. They treated them much as they did the land itself, taking gifts without destroying the giver. Sometimes the trees owned by one tribal member grew inside the hunting preserve used by another, but that was no matter.

The Miwok used the estuary extensively, leaving many shell mounds along the main stream that angled in from the rift valley. They were fond of the shellfish here and feasted on the clams and native oysters, the crabs, and even the octopi that scooted in at night. They used clam shells for trade and money. The heavy shells of the Washington clams were particularly prized. They strung the shells of small rock clams and the little Olivella snails as ornamental beads, and they listened to the roar of the ocean in cockle shells.

It was their custom to take the salmon with nets as well as to spear them. They fished for perch and flounder, too, and the succulent trout. These they might club, or stun with the poison of the wild cucumber placed in quiet pools. The men were strong, and good hunters, but they were not above shooting a cottontail, a gopher or even a skunk with their bows and arrows. It took many men to ring an elk and kill it. When they did, they used every part of the animal, making clothes from the skin, fashioning awls, needles and ornaments from the bones and teeth, and chisels from the antlers. When they had more meat or fish or shellfish than they could eat at one time, they smoked it for later use.

As much as they depended upon the bounty of the land and its waters, the Miwoks spoiled little. There were few of them and they took only what they needed. They left few traces to show that they had used the estuary for many generations, except for their shell mounds and the narrow trails that led across the mountain and up the rift valley, trails hardly more noticeable than those made by the elk and the deer. They left, too, the name *Baulenas* for the little bay inside the white sand spit and for the shores around it. The meaning of that name has been lost in time.

The white men who came to Baulenas were different. They had profoundly different ideas about the land, convictions rooted deep in their traditions. They thought the place was theirs to do with as they chose, and regarded the land as a commodity. As Francis Fletcher, chronicler of Sir Francis Drake's 16th century voyage along these shores, wrote later, the first Europeans found here "a goodly countrie and fruitful soyle, stored with many blessings fit for the use of man."

Which Europeans found the estuary first is uncertain. Some think that Drake himself brought the *Golden Hinde* and its crew of Englishmen into this little bay. The Portuguese and Spanish and other Englishmen who followed may have dropped anchor here. The Russians who pushed down from the north soon after 1800 almost certainly came into the harbor while hunting for fur seal and sea otter. New Englanders, chasing the whales that migrated along these shores, doubtless furled their sails in Baulenas Bay, too, the sailors feasting on the shellfish and drinking the good fresh water that flowed in so conveniently at many places along the shores.

But it was the Spanish, stringing their missions north from Mexico, who laid first official claim to this part of California. They subjected it to their

The waters of the estuary lie quiet and glossy, reflecting the skies, taking on the shades and shapes of the clouds, glowing as though lit from within. Even the faintest wind trails a dark shadow over such a smooth surface.

And the estuary was called Bolinas
Bay. At its southeast end there
was a thick stand of willows that
came to be known as Willow
Camp.

laws and customs, ignoring any prior claim of the Indians. In the early 1800's the Spanish began to dole out parcels of land with a casual hand, often as favors to someone who had served them well. They gave 8,911 acres of Marin County to Rafael Garcia, a young army sergeant. The grant embraced all of the estuary, extending south beyond the sand spit, running east to the ridge top and west to the Pacific. It took in a sizeable chunk of the rift valley as well. Garcia called it Rancho Tomales y Las Baulenas. (If this grant sounds oversized, consider the 35,000-acre ranch just to the north of it, Punta de los Reyes, given to one James Richard Berry, an Irishman and erstwhile colonel in the Mexican Army.) Garcia, who was evidently a better guitarist and horseman than businessman, conveyed his ranch to his brother-in-law, Gregorio Briones, in 1843 and moved his quarters up the rift valley, inaugurating a long-time squabble over land boundaries. Briones renamed the place Rancho Las Baulines.

The first white settlers put the land to use for grazing. They cleared it for fields and set out many head of cattle. The cows did well, and before long there were thousands of them, as well as sheep, horses and swine. So the wolf, the wolverine, the coyote, the mountain lion, and the bear had to go. In 1880, an historian noted: "There was an abundance of California lions and bears in the woods on the East side of the bay. These lions would kill colts and small stock. They were extirpated about 1860." The elk were gone soon, too.

What happened to the estuary itself in those early days was not recorded. The initial impact of grazing on the watersheds is impossible to estimate now. Doubtless there was increased erosion, as well as an additional burden of nutrients washed into the estuary from the fecal wastes of the domestic animals. But however great the change or damage, it was only a small prelude to what was to come.

In 1846, California passed to the United States, and two years later, John August Sutter struck gold in the foothills of the Sierra Nevada. In the stampede that followed, many New Englanders came west. Among them were loggers and shipbuilders, strong and ambitious men. Along with their skill and energy they brought saws and axes, and when they were disappointed in the gold fields, some of them turned to the green gold of California's forests. The redwoods of Baulenas were among the first they found. We can imagine their feelings when they lowered their sails in Baulenas Bay and made their way ashore into the canyons. There stood the ranks of red-barked giants, their massive boles rising from a carpet of delicate clover-like oxalis and unfamiliar ferns to fragment the sunlight into luminous shafts. The men must have stood awestruck. It "was no uncommon thing," the 1880 historian commented, "to find trees fifty feet in circumference, and the lumber was all first class." The trees were equal to any in the state, he added. It was "from Bolinas that the greater part of the early lumber supply for San Francisco came."

The loggers began cutting in 1849. It took two men about a week to bring down a redwood then. They used hand saws and axes and brute strength, and it was slow hard work. Once they felled a giant, they hauled it out with a team of oxen. Some trees were dragged on skid roads; others were laid on carts with wheels made of the cross sections sawed from smaller logs. These wheels cut deep into the soft and vulnerable soil, as did the hooves of the oxen. Gradually, there grew to be a huge spiderweb of skid roads and cart tracks gouged into the slopes around the estuary.

Half a dozen mills sprang up nearby to saw the mammoth logs. Embarcaderos were built along the shore of the estuary. The milled wood was hauled to them, loaded onto barges, and lightered down the lagoon, then transferred to schooners and sailed on to San Francisco where the young metropolis was burgeoning. Redwood was used for wharves and warehouses as well as other buildings. Yet most of the Bolinas redwoods ultimately went up in smoke. At least half of each tree was wasted in the mills, and the other half burned as the city did itself, which was frequently. Shipbuilders soon followed the loggers to take advantage of the good harbor and the ready supply of timber. "There have probably been more vessels built here than at any port of the coast outside of San Francisco," the 1880 scribe observed. A settlement grew up quickly and the "port" boomed.

Near the head of the bay was a hamlet called Dogtown, named for the dogs that chased the elk and bear. It was a happy place, an old logger later reminisced, with dancing and drinking and feasting on elk. There were so many elk, once, that a herd of one thousand was not an uncommon sight up the valley. The Point, where the principal wharves were built, was known first as Jugville, in honor of the principal recreation. In between, along the western shore, was a larger, more permanent village. When Marin county was divided into townships in the early '60's, the village was called Bolinas, the name having been officially anglicized by the U. S. Coastal Service. And the estuary was called Bolinas Bay. At its southeast end there was a thick stand of willows that came to be known as Willow Camp.

The land around Bolinas soon passed into small ownerships. It was fragmented and committed to many uses. Grazing, logging and ship-building were not the only endeavors of those early energetic settlers. They explored every opportunity the land might offer them. They found lime up the rift valley and built kilns in the early '50's. They found copper in Bolinas Ridge and tunnelled in nearly a thousand feet to get it. In 1865 they drilled for oil on the mesa. This was a promising venture, advertised in San Francisco. Anticipating success, the local inn was called The Petroleum Hotel for a few months. When the project failed, rumor had it the boys poured in oil on Saturday night and pumped it out on Sunday for the prospective investors to see.

They also tried their hands at commercial fishing, for the fish were plentiful and delicious. So many trout ran up the little river, first called Gregorio's Creek and later Pine Gulch Creek, that in 1861 the Grinter brothers built fish ponds for the town's first trout farm. The trout were sold in San Francisco.

The hunting was prodigious, not only of elk, deer and the bear, but of wildfowl. After spending a week nearby, a San Franciscan wrote of having "great sport among the duck and wild geese. Their number is told by the hundreds of thousands, and there is little to do but load and fire." Before long, there were duck clubs in the estuary and more city people were loading and firing.

In addition to cutting the big trees in the canyons, the settlers took their axes to the fir and oak, pine and laurel on the ridges, and the alder and willow along the streams. These provided good cordwood, and in two decades half a million cords were lightered out over the bar and sailed to San Francisco. As these trees were cut, there were left, in effect, ready-made open fields to carry more cattle or to put to the plow for potatoes. It took a while to finish off all the forests, but in 1880, the historian wrote: "...the major portion (of trees) has long since been chopped out. The places which knew them shall know them no more forever, nor will others spring up to take their places—Peace be to their ashes."

By that time, the boom town of Bolinas had gone bust. It was not only because the trees were gone. The harbor had been filling in steadily. From what we know now about the effects of logging on Bolinas Ridge—one good storm can wash down as much sediment from a single logged-off canyon as runs off the whole watershed in the course of a full year when the land is left undisturbed—we can infer that heavy silting probably came on hard and quickly once the steep canyons were hit and the big trees skidded out. No one kept a record, but a map of 1858 shows two "old embarcaderos" already high and dry on the estuary's shores after less than a decade of logging. With every canyon being logged, and every hillside, too, with fields being plowed, and with a wagon road carved along the unstable cliff at the estuary's mouth, the scene was set for a massive increase in siltation.

"When vessels first began to sail into this port," according to the history of Bolinas, "a schooner drawing ten feet of water could pass over the bar (across the estuary's mouth) with ease at any stage of the tide, while now the same draught of the vessel can barely pass at the highest stage; and where those large vessels formerly lay at the wharf, the depth of the water will not admit of more than a fishing smack...At the termination of another generation, the record of the many vessels which once spread their canvas in this harbor will read like a fairy tale..." And so it did.

In less than five decades, the white man had done what the red man had not even begun to achieve over thousands of years. He had profoundly altered the land. He had accomplished what the earth itself might have taken many centuries to do. Because of him, the trees were gone, the land was torn and loosened and the estuary was on its way to being old before its time. The wildlife was savaged, and the red man with it. The Coast Miwok was never a match for the European, for his customs, his diseases and his brutality. After the gold rush, "the killing of an Indian was regarded as a sportsmanlike pastime" according to the son of a Marin pioneer. The Miwok numbers dwindled steadily; like the bear, the lion, the elk, and much of the land itself, they were finally "extirpated."

But even with all the changes, the estuary remained, and the shores around it made a pleasant place to live if one liked open country and did not mind looking up at forests of stumps. There was the magic of the constantly moving waters, and the long steady roll of the sea against the nearby coast. There was the towering ridge of the mountain to protect the place, and the fresh feel of fog that so often broke above the small bay, cooling the air but letting a flood of sun pour through. Some people stayed on around Bolinas Bay. They settled down to raising cows and to making cheese and cream and butter.

Bolinas had always been off the beaten track. Even when its harbor was deep enough for ships, the trip into San Francisco by sea was no pleasure sail. Passengers were likely to share the deck with pigs, sheep, cows and horses, and when the going got rough — as it often did in the "potato patch," the shallows off the Golden Gate — everything slid together in a kind of grand mêlée. There was also the dark hook of rocks offshore, Duxbury Reef, waiting to catch unwary sailors when the fog rolled in. It was the scene of many shipwrecks.

For a long time, the trip by land was just as adventurous. At first there were only the Indian trails. In 1849, a traveler went by horse "over the hill" (people today still use the same phrase) and on to Sausalito, where he took a rowboat or a canoe across the bay, likely with strong Indians for his boatmen. When the Briones girl, Maria, married in 1850, she and her sweetheart rode bareback on the same horse into San Rafael to the mission and back in one day (and the whole town danced at the wedding feast that night, on a floor whip-sawed from redwood for the occasion).

Roads were inevitable. The first ran north up the valley to the little village of Olema. It was impassable in wet weather. Wagons sank axle-deep in the mud. By the 1870's, another stage road went to San Rafael. It followed the Indian trail over the mountain's ridge, and the descent to the head of the estuary was memorable. The horses galloped all the way down the narrow winding five-mile stretch, with the stage — a sort of over-grown surrey — swaying and rattling behind them and the passengers hanging on for dear life. The trip uphill was likely to be different. Then passengers might be asked to get out and walk if the road was wet and the horses were slipping. The cuts from this pioneer road are still eroding.

In the last decades of the nineteenth century, railroads became well established in Marin County, and there was a push to run a spur from Mill Valley to Willow Camp and Bolinas. It was the era of the seashore spa, and the idea was to make the Bolinas sand spit "the Coney Island of the West," as the Sausalito *News* phrased it. In 1902, a wagon road was cut from West Point Inn, halfway up the south slope of Mt. Tamalpais, around to Willow Camp, by then a growing summer resort. The Mt. Tamalpais Railroad Company built this eight-mile roadbed for five thousand dollars. A few years later, tracks were laid along it for a few miles, but this railroad spur was never completed.

The road did occasion heavier summer use around Bolinas and Stinson Beach, as Willow Camp was coming to be known. Cabanas sprouted along the Bolinas beach and groins were laid to build up the sand. At the Flagstaff Inn (successor to the Petroleum Inn) rates were twelve dollars a week for room and meals, half that for children, and nine dollars for a nurse. At the turn of the century the inn had a telephone and the town had a good livery stable and blacksmith shop. The hunting and fishing were superb. A small party might take nearly six hundred smelt on an August afternoon. All this was only five hours from San Francisco by stage and railroad and ferry, and the round trip fare was three and a half dollars, everything included.

As human use around Bolinas Bay increased, there were increasing demands on the local fresh water supply. The mountain offered a source of water in every canyon; the high ridge, itself, was deeply saturated. People

The land ethic which had brought this place and estuaries all over the world to the point of destruction…is based on the anthropocentric belief that the earth and its resources were put here primarily for people…Man makes the rules. It is an ethic… based on false assumptions.

sank wells, and there were many springs around the town. But as more and more water was needed and taken, first for Bolinas and then for Stinson Beach, less and less sweet water reached the estuary. There was also the problem of human sewage disposal. Soon after the new century began, it became acute. Bolinas set up a Sanitary District, the town's first official body. (Since the town has never incorporated, the directors of its utility district—which today covers water as well as sewage—remain the "town fathers.")

In 1905, a sewage system was designed, said to be the best in the state. The raw sewage would empty into the mouth of the estuary's channel, discharged by a special flap valve at ebb tide, to be carried out to sea. Whether the sewage might be carried back in on flood tide was not considered a serious factor. Concrete was poured for the new sewers behind a store down town, but before the line could be laid in 1906, the great earthquake struck.

On the morning of April 18, just north of Bolinas, the land of the mesa lurched northwest thirteen and a half feet and sank about a foot lower on the east. The hamlet of Bolinas, according to a San Francisco newspaper, was "ravaged by the tremblor." Almost every building along the estuary's shore toppled into the water. Chimneys fell and china broke in other parts of town. But no one was killed. People picked up the pieces, propped up the buildings, and went about the business of laying the new sewer. That same year, they suffered a holocaust of fire on the mountain's ridge —one of the many wild fires that raged through the cutover forests, re-moving the ground cover and adding to the sedimentation. This one raced from the top of the ridge to the bay's eastern shore in a matter of minutes. Only the heroic efforts of the local people saved the homes along the shore. Not long after this, the town obtained its first real water system and fire hydrants.

By 1911, traffic was sluggish in the shallow harbor. Perhaps by coincidence, maps were now calling it Bolinas Lagoon instead of Bolinas Bay. Only the gasoline schooner, the *Owl*, and the sailing vessel, *Jenny Griffin*, ran regularly into San Francisco. A Stanley Steamer had replaced the old horse stage.

In the second decade of this century, land on the mesa was put to a new use. The Marconi Company chose it for the site of a large transmitting and receiving station. Building supplies were sailed into Bolinas Lagoon, unloaded at the wharves and skidded up the mesa on horse-drawn sleds that plowed up the land afresh. During this decade there were several spectacular shipwrecks on Duxbury Reef, and in 1917 the U.S. Coast Guard built a station on Wharf Road in Bolinas. About the same time, the channel of Pine Gulch Creek was relocated and the delta was filled to gain new pastureland along the shore. The estuary's island—called Kent Island for its owner—was growing larger, and trees were beginning to flourish there. Soon the road around the estuary was widened and paved. The canyon's free-running streams were encased in concrete culverts, the wet meadows in the alluvial fans cut off from the estuary. Banks were sliced back, and fill was brought in and dumped along the shore.

In 1926, the San Francisco *Bulletin* offered lots—20' x 100'—on the mesa

The hunting was prodigious. After spending a week nearby, a San Franciscan wrote of "having great sport among the duck and wild geese.... There is nothing to do but load and fire."

for $69.50, plus a six month's subscription to the newspaper. Payment was $9.50 down and only three dollars a month thereafter, a full page ad said, and first come first served. It was an ingenious money-making scheme. Everyone would profit—the local landowner, the newspaper, and most of all the New York promoters who dreamed it all up, and repeated it elsewhere. As it turned out, the *Bulletin* ended up giving away lots to get new subscribers during the depression a few years later. And the land was subdivided like a giant sheet of postage stamps; nearly sixty-five hundred lots in all were committed to an impossible pattern of use. Both the town of Bolinas and the county had the increasing headaches of providing necessary services, such as water (taken at first directly from the Bolinas water supply) and roads. Bolinas would not again be the same.

About this time people began to notice that the Pine Gulch Creek delta and the mud flats offshore had silted up so high that the flushing action of the inpouring fresh water was diminished badly. Circulation in the shallower parts of the estuary was slower than it had been. The water was becoming stagnant in places, and new marshes were forming along the shores and the lee side of Kent Island. There was no official recognition of these changes, and nothing was done about them. Bolinas Beach began to have problems, too. By the early 'forties there was no sand exposed at high tide and almost none at low. Swimming was difficult. This prompted property owners to take up a subscription to build two large new groins, one lying along the northern limits of the estuary's channel. Whether this affected the estuary's circulation adversely—or not at all—was not considered either.

During World War II it was rumored that the United States Navy was eyeing Bolinas Lagoon for a secret submarine base, but nothing came of it —although enemy submarines were sunk offshore and one live mine washed onto the sand spit and occasioned great excitement when the Coast Guard detonated it. It was among the last things the Coast Guard did here; soon after the war, they gave up their base, leaving a set of buildings which the College of Marin would acquire and later use for a marine station.

It was inevitable that Bolinas Lagoon would share in the postwar boom that struck California. Though it still lay off the beaten track, the roads in were highly scenic, and soon the area became a mecca for Sunday drivers. The swimming at Stinson Beach proved to be the best in the whole Bay Area, far better and less dangerous than at San Francisco's Ocean Beach. As the regional population spiraled, thousands flocked to Stinson Beach every sunny Sunday. The town itself began to build up, more and more fresh water was needed and taken from the mountain's drainage, and more sewage was produced.

Before long, developers were eyeing Bolinas Lagoon itself. One imaginative promotor wanted to fill it for a race track since it was just naturally shaped that way. Another suggested that Kent Island be used as a football field for exhibition games. A more practical proposal was to grow oysters, and in the 1950s, an oyster farm went into production in the estuary. It was a shock to the operators to find that the waters were so polluted that the oysters were inedible. The venture was dropped, but it left a few Japanese oysters as new members of the estuary's benthic community.

Soon the Bolinas sand spit was formally subdivided. The southern end became a California state park, the northern, an exclusive residential development with a locked gate and its own private ocean beach. The estuary was dredged extensively on the lee side of the spit to make an artificial enclosed lagoon for new homes to front upon. Both developments meant more demands for water and more headaches for the sanitary engineers.

And despite obvious warning signals that the carrying capacity of the Bolinas-Stinson Beach area was being strained, people went on trying to develop it further. Small boat owners, in particular, were vocal in demands that the estuary be dredged and made into a small boat harbor. In 1956, the state—nominally responsible for all its tidelands—responded by creating the Bolinas Harbor District to administer the estuary locally, control its use, and plan for orderly and substantial development. Directors were elected, and they immediately initiated a series of technical, scientific and ecological studies of the place. So much work was done on Bolinas Lagoon during the next decade that it ended up being called the world's most studied estuarine area.

Five years later, the Bay Area Regional Water Pollution Control Board, the Marin County Health Department and the California State Department of Public Health unwittingly marked the 125th anniversary of Rafael Garcia's land grant by issuing the first of a series of "Cease and Desist" orders forbidding the dumping of raw sewage into Bolinas Lagoon. Thus did the estuary celebrate a century and a quarter of use by civilized man. That same year, Marin County adopted a master plan calling for increased urban development of Bolinas and Stinson Beach, more commercial recreation facilities, and more roads. And when Point Reyes National Seashore was established nearby, there were more arguments for better access, for a multi-lane freeway or at least a "scenic highway" along Bolinas Ridge to "open up" new views for Sunday drivers. Although either road would have destroyed the estuary, both went on the drawing boards of the highway engineers.

In 1966, after ten years of studies, the Bolinas Harbor District presented a formal plan for the development of Bolinas Lagoon. It called for an elaborate small-boat and recreational complex, with facilities including sixteen hundred berths, a hotel, restaurants, a landing strip for small planes, even a mini-wilderness area, to be built into Bolinas Lagoon—directly on the San Andreas Fault.

Had the plan been offered a few years earlier, it might have been embraced with enthusiasm. Even its severest critics called it highly ingenious and efficient in putting to use every square inch of the estuary's 1,100 acres. As it was, however, it caused an unexpected uproar. During the 1960s, conservation forces had been gathering strength in Marin County, reflecting a growing national trend. Now many local people, both longtime residents and a swelling tide of newcomers, were ready to speak out against this kind of development, however well done. They had enough clout to recall the Harbor District directors in 1968 and to dump the plan. The next year, the state turned over Bolinas Lagoon to Marin County, which promptly initiated another study, this time calling on the Conservation Foundation for help. In the middle of this study, logging of second-growth redwoods on Bolinas Ridge caused another local furor. In an unprecedented action, the county called the logging to a halt.

With the coming of the 'seventies, the crises around Bolinas Lagoon began to peak. In the summer of 1970, infectious hepatitis became epidemic in the town of Bolinas. The shellfish of the estuary were found to be heavily contaminated with the responsible virus, which is carried in sewage. Bolinas Lagoon and its offshore waters were quarantined. The sewage problem was now crucial. The local utility directors and the county, state, and federal officials, agreed that Bolinas and Stinson Beach should have a regional disposal system.

The San Francisco Bay oil spill of January 18, 1971 precipitated another emergency. Ocean currents carried quantities of bunker oil slowly and inexorably along the coast toward Bolinas. Soon the residents were joined by an inpouring of Bay Area young people in a frantic effort to save the life of the estuary. Booms were strung across the channel, hay was dumped in by the bale to soak up oil. Swimmers in wet suits or blue jeans plunged into the offshore waters to rescue oil-soaked birds. The College of Marin Marine Station became a hospital for the injured birds and headquarters for many of the workers. To some longtime residents, it seemed that they were being invaded by an army of hippies. To other people, the battle of the oil spill was at once discouraging and inspiring. Despite heroic efforts to save the oil-soaked birds, most of them died; and oil got into the estuary. But having shared in what became weeks of grueling physical labor, the workers formed strong bonds among themselves. When the debacle was over, they set up a new community action group — Bolinas Future Studies.

In the November 1971 election of utility district directors for Bolinas and Stinson Beach, the new group took over. Both towns had been split over the regional sewage system finally proposed: in line with the county's Master Plan, it was designed to accommodate an eventual population of 25,000 people. In another stunning show of strength, local conservationists recalled incumbent utility district directors who favored regional sewage disposal, and elected a majority of young activists who strongly opposed it. The new town fathers scrapped the sewage plan and began studies for separate recycling plants in Bolinas and Stinson Beach. In Bolinas, they also imposed a moratorium on issuing water meters, effectively stopping all new building. The next step was to have the county's Master Plan repealed, which they did. Other problems facing them around this small west coast estuary would not be so readily dealt with.

There was Bolinas Lagoon itself, and what should be done with it, and by whom. So short a time ago it had been a well-watered living bay, deep enough for schooners to enter on the lowest tides. Now it was a wetland with ever more shallow and stagnant waters, and tidal flats colored bright green with the tell-tale algae born of eutrophication. A victim of misuse and overuse for thirteen decades, it had suffered most of the classic depredations accorded to estuaries all over the world. Although it had escaped being mined or "reclaimed," its watersheds had been profoundly altered, the forests stripped, the land plowed up or converted to pasture. Two towns stood on its shores, took its fresh water and dumped their waste into it. A heavily

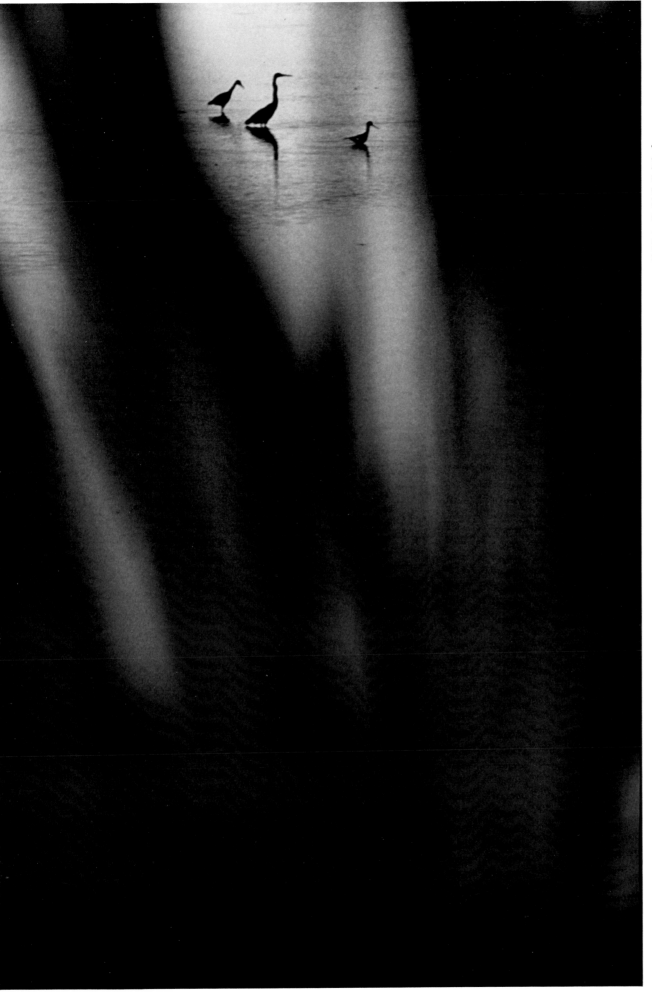

The San Francisco Bay oil spill of January 18, 1971, precipitated another emergency. Ocean currents carried quantities of bunker oil slowly and inexorably along the coast toward Bolinas. …Swimmers in wet suits or blue jeans plunged into the waters to rescue oil-soaked birds.

used resort and a subdivision occupied its adjacent beach and took its fresh water, too. Not only were the estuary's waters polluted by human and bovine waste, its shellfish were pathogenic. Its shores were rimmed with a paved road with shoulders frequently sprayed with pesticides. Its basin had been dredged and filled in many places, and one end had been diked off to make a separate lagoon. Much of the wildlife which once flourished around the estuary had been extinguished, along with the native people. Civilized man, an unwitting geological force and agent of ecological and evolutionary change, had left his inescapable marks.

Despite it all, this particular estuary had managed to retain a loveliness and serenity, an elemental kind of beauty. Some of its logged-off redwood canyons had regenerated so well that people wanted to cut the new trees. Some of the lands of its watersheds had healed themselves. Herons and egrets had chosen a canyon here for their rookery. The wetlands were a favored stop on the Pacific Flyway for tens of thousands of birds. And as a measure of what we have generally done to our land, Bolinas Lagoon was now being referred to as one of the last "relatively unspoiled" estuaries along the California coast.

Not only did Marin County propose to keep it as an "ecological preserve," the state of California now wanted it for a state park. There was strong conservation support for the federal government to include a large section of its watersheds in the proposed Golden Gate National Recreation Area, a grand open-space complex which, it was hoped, would stretch from the Golden Gate to Point Reyes. And members of the new establishment in Bolinas and Stinson Beach, being strong proponents of local option, wanted to decide the future of Bolinas Lagoon themselves.

If they succeeded in wresting this prize from the jurisdiction of the county or the state, they would be faced by some serious questions. Lovely as it was, Bolinas Lagoon was slowly dying: if left alone it would probably be a marshy meadow in a matter of decades, barring a major earthquake. Should people, descendants perhaps of those who had brought it to its present condition, interfere? Should a try be made to reverse the processes initiated decades ago? Should the basin be dredged to increase the circulation, and flood control attempted to diminish the present heavy sedimentation? The answers to these questions, among many others, would call for sensitivity and expertise. Where to start meddling — and, more importantly, where to stop — would be delicate decisions.

Adding to the dilemma was the fact that this estuary, like so many other land forms, had long been considered and treated as a separate entity existing in a kind of vacuum. Legally defined as a tideland, its boundaries were described by the high tide line: almost all plans for its disposition stopped at its very edges. Yet it was, of course, an integral part of the watersheds around it. Its ultimate fate was tied, as it had always been, to the fate of these lands. Ideally, a rational overall land-use policy which would consider the different parts of the landscape in the context of the whole would be developed and implemented. But this would be costly and time-consuming, and there was no governmental agency to handle it.

The Bolinas Mesa subdivision raised other issues. There were still over 500 lots only 20′ x 100′ in size, and another 800 lots were 40′ x 100′.

Twilight is a time of enchantment. The sunsets here are often vividly colored, with sheaves of clouds stained yellow and crimson and coral.

Houses had been built at will—often in marshy areas. The grid of roads originally carved into the mesa had totally disregarded drainage patterns; the land was now deeply rutted and eroded in many places. Much of the area demanded rehabilitation. And future development would need careful control. While a moratorium on water meters might buy time to seek solutions to problems such as these, it was clearly no final answer. Again ideally, the carrying capacity of the mesa as well as the surrounding areas would be measured before further development took place. But again, there was no money—nor governmental mechanism—for such a study.

At the same time the community leaders were struggling with the heritage of this impossible subdivision, they had to deal with the hard reality of other established uses. As in many places, unrestricted and unplanned-for use was now deeply entrenched. And the thousands of people who kept on demanding this fragile place for their pleasure thought it was their right. In a world accustomed to accommodating such human pressures by building more roads, bringing in more water, and so forth, it would be no easy thing to innovate the changes necessary to rescue the area.

While the problems centered around this small west coast estuary were unique to the place itself, they typified in one degree or another the kind of land use problems confronting people around many other estuaries. Back of them lay a far graver problem—the land ethic which had brought this place and estuaries all over the world to the point of destruction. This ethic is based on the anthropocentric belief that the earth and its resources were put here primarily for people, for their use, enjoyment, and exploitation. It sets people apart from the land and other living creatures. It gives them "dominion" over the earth. It requires that everything be measured in terms of human utility. It also assumes that people are in control, and able to do what they choose. Man makes the rules. It is an ethic as old as civilization and it has occasioned the fall as well as the rise of glorious cultures. For it is based on false assumptions.

The earth does not belong to us: we belong to it. We are subject to the same immutable laws that govern all living things. We are no more in ultimate control of the earth than we are of our own life-spans.

To accept this fact—so contrary to cherished traditions; to come to understand earth's laws and to write our own laws within them; to live with the land, not off it—these are the real challenges facing the people deciding the fate of Bolinas Lagoon, and estuaries everywhere.

An old road leads to the house where I stay when I am in Bolinas. It curves up the hill between shrubs and pines and eucalyptus trees, taking the easiest way to gain the height of the mesa above the shore, fitting itself discreetly into the land. It lends itself well to walking.

It is most pleasant at night. The darkness heightens my awareness of the smells and sounds around me. The sea's faint salty fragrance mingles with the scent of green plants breathing and the incense of the eucalyptus. My feet make a soft scuffle in the dirt, stirring the grains of siltstone laid down in an ancient estuary. A chorus of frog-song stops when I pass too close to a wet meadow, and then begins again when I cross the mysterious boundary of the singers' territory. I hear an owl's lonely cry.

At the top of the hill, there is a small clearing rimmed with eucalyptus trees. I pause for a while to watch the sky fill up with stars. Some seem close enough to be tangled in the trailing branches, yet I know that the light of the nearest star has traveled for years to reach my eyes. I ponder the phenomenon of that light which traces a vast, incomprehensible dimension of space. It forms almost a tangible bond between myself and the shimmering galaxy to which I belong. I consider the marvel of the human eye that accepts that light, and the mind that comprehends it and relates it to space and time and self.

What wonderful creatures we humans are, with our eyes and minds — and almost infinite capacities. How curious and sad that somewhere along the line we seem to have lost our reverence and understanding of the earth. We live so much of our lives as aliens from the land. We war on the land, pillage it, and try to bend it to our will. And we diminish ourselves thereby, perhaps far more than we know.

Feeling very much a part of the night, the silt I stand upon, and the stars I watch, I marvel that my body is made from the same kinds of atoms that form the stars, the seas, marsh grasses and the spiraled shells of moon snails. I recall words written by astronomer Harlow Shapley: "We are... brothers of the boulders, cousins of the clouds, distant kin...of the...plants and animals that in times past took a try, as we are now doing, at life and persistence."

If we are to succeed at that try, we must pause to redefine ourselves and our place on this small planet that is our home. We must learn again to revere the earth and live in harmony with it.

Surely, I think as I walk on down the road under the arching canopy of trees, seeing the faint glimmer of the estuary where its waters lap the shore below — surely there is no better place to begin than here.

Should you chance to visit an unspoiled estuary, treat it gently, recalling
that it is fragile, easily disarranged and destroyed by too many people,
or by people who do not care. Touch no living thing. Walk quietly.
Look, listen, and enjoy the place. And let it be.

Notes on ecology
References &
Acknowledgements

Notes on ecology

A wise man once observed that we cannot do just one thing. When we cut the trees off the lands of a watershed, for instance, we set into motion a chain of related events: we increase the erosion of the soil; we alter the pattern of run-off of the waters; we change wetlands fed by the land's waters. This is because, of course, everything on earth is hitched together (as John Muir and Robert Browning, among others, noted long ago). Nothing exists alone. All life forms and land forms are intricately and inextricably linked into a continuum. They are not linked haphazardly, but according to certain elemental and immutable laws. Ecology is the science that considers these laws.

As I began to put this book together, I soon concluded that the estuary—of all land forms—should not, indeed could not, be considered alone as though it existed in a kind of vacuum. To begin with, the estuary is itself composed of other distinct land forms, of watersheds and rivers and shores and tides. It is furthermore the site of many processes which are essential to the survival of countless life forms. It is also a place where many of earth's elemental ecological laws may be seen dynamically at work. I soon found myself looking at the estuary from the broader, ecological point of view, describing it as a place vital in earth's total scheme of things.

And as I researched the subject, delving into microbiology, botany, ornithology, marine biology, astronomy, and geology, among other disciplines, I realized I was, in fact, gaining a wider perspective and understanding of ecology. For ecology is a synthesis of all the earth and life sciences. It uses whichever of them it needs in its grand overview of life's inter-relationship with earth.

This section grew from some of my notes. It is a short discussion of ecology, of some of its basic ideas and principles, and of various fundamental ecological laws. It is selective, indeed eclective, and often oversimplified. Necessarily. The study of ecology can consume a lifetime and still leave certain things unexplored. And this is not meant to be even a short textbook on ecology. For those who are familiar with the science and with the ecological role of the estuary, what follows may be superfluous. For those who approach the subject of the estuary—and ecology—from scratch (as I did), it will serve as a frame of reference for many parts of this book.

ECOLOGY may be defined simply as the science which deals with living organisms and their environment. It shares its root—the Greek word *oikos*, meaning *home*—with the word *economy*. Literally, ecology is the study of the home. Life's home, the ecosphere—sometimes called the biosphere.

THE ECOSPHERE is the bubble of air and soil and water that encases the earth. It is a thin bubble. It includes the soil to a depth of only a few feet and the air to the height it can be breathed and sustain life, perhaps 30,000 feet (although tiny insects, viable seeds and spores are found floating somewhat higher). When measured against the mass of the planet, it is seen to be an exceedingly small fraction of it.

The ecosphere is tough, having evolved and survived throughout billions of years. It is also very fragile. Its air and soil and water can be easily fouled and poisoned, and since they are interrelated and move constantly into and out of one another, poisons can be quickly circulated and become universal. The mechanisms of its life systems can also be easily upset, for they are in delicate balance with one another. The ecosphere is irreplacable. It contains all the life that we have discovered anywhere.

Within life's home there are many rooms. They are often described as ecosystems.

AN ECOSYSTEM is a community of animals and plants living together in a particular physical environment or habitat. Sometimes the ecosphere is described as earth's ecosystem, and in the broader sense the two words are interchangeable. Most often, however, an ecosystem refers to a particular part of the ecosphere or to a particular land form—a pond, a tidepool, a redwood forest, an alpine meadow, or an estuary. Although ecosystems need and interact with each other, each runs by itself, each is different, each has its own habitats and communities.

A HABITAT is any specific physical environment where plants and animals live together. It is often used in the broad sense. There is the marine habitat and the terrestrial habitat. More narrowly, a habitat may be a particular place or it may even be composed primarily of living things. A forest of seaweed provides the habitat for many plants and animals. So does a stand of grasses in a salt marsh, and a bed of mussels in a bay. In one bed of mussels, for example, 30 different species of plants and animals have been found coexisting.

AN ECOTONE, or edge, where habitats or ecosystems touch and merge, is most often a particularly rich place, having the best of the two worlds it joins. Along such an interface, there is more encounter and exchange, a greater variety of life. More happens. Life in shallow waters is more abundant than in the deep open sea. The plants and animals can take advantage of the substrate—land—good light, the water, and the shore. The greater abundance and variety of life in an ecotone results from what is called the EDGE EFFECT.

A NICHE (from the Latin, *nidus* or *nest,* via the French, *niche,* a place in which to put a statue) is the ecological role a species fills in its ecosystem. As ecologist Eugene Odum puts it, if the habitat of a species is its "address," its niche is its "profession." It is a biological law that where there is an open or unfilled niche, an established species will fill it, or a new species will evolve to do so. A niche is almost never filled by two species, since the more successful and stronger of the two will crowd out the weaker—the "survival of the fittest" principle.

Many plants and animals have evolved to fill earth's countless niches, and many have created new niches in the process, as the bed of mussels did, ending up with 30 niches in its midst. The important thing is that every living plant and animal on earth fills a particular niche in its ecosystem—and ultimately in the ecosphere. Each has a role to play and a reason for being. Man is very adept at altering and destroying niches, as he does when he cuts down trees, bulldozes the land or fills an estuary.

A SPECIES is a unique life form, a plant or animal group unlike any other. A species may be closely related to other life forms which belong to its *GENUS*, and there may be many *GENERA* in one of life's many *FAMILIES*. People with tidy minds like to arrange earth's life forms further, classifying them into *PHYLA* and so on—ending ultimately with the basic division:

plants and animals. Beyond them lie the viruses and bacteria which are neither plant nor animal.

The total number of individuals of a species living in a particular habitat or ecosystem makes *A POPULATION*. Populations, not individuals, fill niches. A number of different populations living together make up a *COMMUNITY*.

Communities and ecosystems are never static. Nothing in nature stays still. Species constantly change and evolve new characteristics. (Change and time are two sides of the same coin, and time it should be noted, is the dimension of evolution.) Earth and its processes are prime agents of change. Volcanic eruptions, fires, wind, rain, and the seasons themselves all bring change. Winter tightens the land with cold. Summer lets it sprawl free. Water or its absence is a prime agent of change. Storms, floods and drought constantly alter the earth. And consider how water invades the crannies of granite, freezes and thaws, working the rocks, loosening them, changing them ultimately into particles of soil.

Forever changing, life itself is a major agent of change. Living communities alter their own habitats in the very process of living. Often it is a slow and subtle change, not obvious at all, but over months and years it may be so profound that the original community can no longer survive. Life forms in a pond, for instance, add to its organic content, slowly contributing to the silting of the water. The pond becomes a meadow. The meadow welcomes the seeds of trees and it, in turn, becomes a forest. Plant life in an estuary helps trap sediments and build up soil until the estuary becomes a marsh and then a coastal plain.

This changing procession of interacting communities and habitats is called a *SUCCESSION*. After many successions, a balanced community may evolve in a particular place, like the tundra, without changing it rapidly or profoundly. This is a *CLIMAX COMMUNITY*. Climax communities are especially well adapted. They exist in perfect balance with their environment. The energy exchange is in equilibrium. Once destroyed, it may take millennia to rebuild a climax community.

A *LIMITING FACTOR* is the presence or absence—or too much or too little—of any element required for life's survival. Limiting factors are often physical, and many are universal. There is the matter of space, for example, which all life forms require. There is the need for shelter. There is water, which every living cell requires. Life may lock itself into dry spores or seeds for decades or even centuries, but it must have water to be born again. There is the requirement for light, shared by all green plants and many animals, and, equally, there is the need for dark. There is the limitation or the *CARRYING CAPACITY* of a place, an ecosystem (or the ecosphere). Only so much life can be nourished and sustained by the resources which are present within finite bounds. There is temperature. Life can survive within only a comparatively narrow range. Even the simplest forms of bacteria perish when it gets too hot or too cold.

Limiting factors can be biological, as when one species depends upon another. The association may be *PARASITIC*, where one life form, the parasite, harms the other, the host; *COMMENSAL*, where neither life form harms the other, or *MUTUALISTIC*, where the two life forms depend upon one another for survival and cannot live apart. In mutualism, the most pressing limiting factor is the presence or absence of the partner. For example, man needs certain bacteria living with him to help with his digestive processes and to manufacture the vitamins he needs to survive. His body, in turn, provides the bacteria a home.

Man, too, of course, and all other living things, must have food. The presence or absence of green plants is an elemental limiting factor for all animals, which depend ultimately upon plants for life.

A more subtle limiting factor is COMPETITION. Success or failure in getting a space, staking a territory, finding food, filling the right niche—these spell the difference between the life and death of individuals and species. Competition controls the size of populations and encourages natural selection, and thereby plays a role in evolution.

Two of the many rules that underlie limiting factors may be noted here. Life forms are most vulnerable when they are immature, not only because they may be small and helpless, but because they have a narrower RANGE OF TOLERANCE than adults. Life forms with a wide range of tolerance are more successful, and may be ubiquitous. Certain grasses, for instance, have a range of tolerance wide enough to let them live in salty water. They grow on salt marshes in temperate climates all over the world. Their range of tolerance for climate is not quite so wide. In tropical zones they give way to mangrove communities.

Life has indeed invented an elegant system of checks and balances to keep the ecosphere in working order. The ability of plants and animals to adapt to limiting factors is one of the foremost among them.

One of the most basic limiting factors of all is the availability of the chemical elements, or NUTRIENTS, on which life depends. Life requires in overwhelming quantity the stuff of stars—hydrogen, carbon, oxygen and nitrogen—and these are the most abundant in the ecosphere. But in curious and subtle ways, life is hitched to other elements, demanding less of them, sometimes only a trace. All DNA, the essential nucleic acid in living cells, must have phosphorous to build its magnic structure. Each molecule of chlorophyll requires a single atom of magnesium for its "heart." In every molecule of hemoglobin, the blood's red cell, there must be exactly four atoms of iron. Every protein needs atoms of sulfur to firm its shape, and without them would flop as limp as a wilted flower stem.

Atoms of all the elements on earth are in limited—and often short—supply. We live in a closed system.

A CLOSED SYSTEM is a finite place, with finite resources. A terrarium, for example, is a closed system. So is a submarine, a spaceship, and, of course, planet earth. Recently, the full implications of what a closed system means to man has become clear to him.

During the course of human history, there have been a few moments of truth so brilliant and profound they have illumined and changed the rest of human thought. There was the moment when Copernicus discerned the solar system and earth's place in it, when Newton defined the laws of gravity, when Darwin perceived the origin of species. In our time there was the moment when man first looked back at his planet home from outer space. He saw a little jewel-like globe, glowing green and blue and streaked with swirls of clouds and storms. It turned slowly in a great black void of space, lovely and vulnerable and alone, carrying on the shimmering veil of its surface all the life we know in the universe.

In this, our closed system, we have no supply lines to any other planet, no replacements available for any of earth's parts. Being limited in number, the molecules of the land and air and water must by cycled and recycled, used and re-used. The air we breathe has been breathed countless times before, by birds, by fish, by ancient dinosaurs, by men two thousand years ago and since and long before. It has passed countless times through plants, through forests, and oceans, and will again. Our most distant descendants will breathe it anew. The calcium in our bones has moved along the courses of continents, flowing with great rivers into deltas and estuaries and shallow seas where microorganisms and filter feeders have concentrated it, and forams have formed it into tiny spiral shells and returned it to the food chain. The water in our bodies has traveled through trees and seas, through lakes and storms, through countless forms of life. And our air and water and soil and all that we are will pass on to new forms of life we will never know. There is no substitute for any of the elements essential to life in the closed system of the ecosphere.

The earth helps to *CYCLE* and *RECYCLE* these precious elements. The air forms a huge storage pool for certain elements, for nitrogen and carbon and oxygen, in particular, and for ozone which shields life from the full spectrum of the sun's rays. The sea and the estuary collect all the elements, water molecules having peculiar abilities to hitch up with other kinds of molecules.

The land itself is a storage bin of nutrients. It has the alchemy of its own soils (many laid down by the sea), and it catches the drift borne on air and winds, and pulled down by rain. Tides, currents, winds, storms, and all earth's moving waters—rivers, rains, and even the spray of waves—are great agents of cycling.

Working with the earth are many plants and animals which are essential to maintaining the great cycles. In the nitrogen cycle, for instance, the nitrogen which makes up some eighty percent of the air must be "fixed" into a form usable by life. Certain algae, fungi, and bacteria are designed to carry out this task, and they alone perform it. Once fixed, the nitrates are used by plants and enter into the animal food chain where they are excreted in a different form as urea and ammonia. Again, certain microorganisms alter these compounds so that they can be used again. Other bacteria are equipped to perform the opposite function; they put nitrogen back into the air.

Phosphates do not drift in the air, but after passing through many forms of life are washed eventually into the sea, where they sink into the cold and heavy bottom waters. The sea, moving to its own slow rhythm, turns over its waters once in a millennium, upwelling phosphates and other nutrients it has collected in its deeps. The phytoplankton or floating plants in cold upwelled waters are then well supplied, and put the phosphates back in circulation, but carriers are needed to return this essential substance onto the land. Shad, salmon, trout, and other anadramous fish carry phosphates (and other nutrients) inland when they return to their birthplaces to spawn and die. Birds also cycle phosphates—and nitrates—concentrating them in guano on many offshore rocks and in the wetlands along their migratory flyways.

In close-knit partnership, then, the earth and its plants and animals join in the necessary process of cycling and recycling the precious elements life demands. Nutrients and minerals are kept moving constantly throughout the ecosphere, threading back and forth between living and nonliving things, changing form, changing shape, joining with other elements and separating out again, on their often long and intricate journey through time. In the closed system of the ecosphere, nothing is ultimately wasted, nothing is ultimately lost.

Man, however, by meddling with the natural sequence of the great cycles, and by fiddling with his precious nutrients, may make certain elements unavailable for human use for unknown lengths of time. He may be doing this, for instance, by using phosphate for detergent and then dumping it into his rivers, estuaries and lakes. This phosphate opens up new niches for green algae, which in turn open new niches for bacteria. The bacteria exhaust the oxygen in the water by their life processes, all life dies, and the phosphate is out of circulation. No one knows how long it will take to put things back into order. (We can never do just one thing.)

To power life, and the earth itself, there must, of course, be ENERGY. And as primitive man recognized dimly, watching the fiery arc of the sun and feeling its good warmth on his skin, the sun is the ultimate source of energy on earth. It is the giver of life. It heats our air and land and water, making a livable world. It propels our winds and the ocean's currents and helps pull our tides. It generates the power in green plants, and it is the power of green plants that runs all other living things. It is a natural law that energy can be neither created nor destroyed. It may be captured and converted, harnessed and used or stored (as it is in oil and other fossil fuel), but never manufactured. Like the elements of the earth, it is in finite supply and we receive our limited quota of sunlight every day. But unlike the elements, energy cannot be recycled. It pours through life in a great one-way flood, coursing swiftly, returning ultimately to space.

Our solar energy, like the stuff of life, is a gift of the universe. Locked into the dust of ancient stars that formed our galaxy, it sprays now from the glowing mass of our sun, radiating into space, drenching the planets and their moons. Only on earth is it seized and held and used for life as we know it. The unique act of capture occurs in the cells of earth's green plants.

Green is the color of life. Over the land and through the waters of the earth there is woven a continuous mesh of green plants, growing in hundreds and thousands of shapes and sizes and forms. There are the one-celled algae. Simple, primitive and eternal, they live everywhere: in snow, in steaming hot springs, on the barks of trees and the clay of flower pots, in the ooze of marsh ponds, on and in the muds and sands of estuaries, and they swarm through earth's waters in teeming billions, subject to the vagaries of winds and tides and the moods of rivers, lakes, estuaries and seas.

And where the algae stop the mosses and liverworts begin. Holding their fruiting bodies like tiny parasols, they cover the earth's wet and shadowy places, fringing streams and softening rocks with their velvety emerald greens. With them grow the ferns, the universal plants that tuft forest floors, drape themselves on banks and sprawl along roadsides and in open meadows. The forests above them reach higher for the sun while the shrubs of the understory accept the leftover light in their dim-green world.

And everywhere on earth, in sunlit and shady places, floating on lakes, stitching down sands and silts and shores and marshes and meadows, twining their stems through woods, studding fields, pinning themselves to granite peaks and streaming in estuarine waters, there are the flowering plants, grasses and succulents, vines and shrubs, and all the vast assortment of herbs. They riot over the earth in an endless exquisite embroidery.

It is an extraordinary statement of nature's ingenuity and inventiveness, this paisley of green plants that drapes the planet. And it is far more. It is a great green global grid which traps and fixes the energy of the sun as earth moves through its radiant light. No denser anywhere than the depth of a tree's branches or the thickness of a leaf or blade of grass, as tenuous as the upper film of sunlit water where the phytoplankton float, this grid generates all of the energy for life on earth. For in every green plant cell, in skeins of pigment or packed into tiny discs and stacked in strange little batteries is chlorophyll, the magic stuff with the secret of photosynthesis, the ability to make food from light.

In *PHOTOSYNTHESIS*, a green plant cell fastens the energy of sunlight into a usable food, sugar. Using the reds and blues of light (the green rays are not absorbed and so give plants their color) chlorophyll takes carbon dioxide (CO_2) out of the air and water (H_2O), a few crucial elements from the soil, and forms carbohydrate and, as a by-product, oxygen. It is essentially a rearrangement of the molecules of star stuff. This energy-binding process, a feat of physical engineering and chemical skill, is more remarkable than all the contrivances of man, who for all his expertise, cannot duplicate it. It remains the province of small mindless green cells, of microscopic scraps of protoplasm, of all the world's grasses and trees and shrubs and flowers that need only sit in the sun.

The evolution of green plants, which began some three billion years ago, brought about the air we breathe. With the greening of the earth the first free oxygen drifted into the atmosphere, and the way was prepared for animals, too, to evolve. And so to the green plants we owe the food we eat, the air we breathe and, often, the fuel we burn. They power the flight of egrets, the leap of the flashing fish and, ultimately, the beat of the human heart.

As plants and animals use the energy captured in photosynthesis, they release carbon dioxide and hydrogen in the process of *RESPIRATION*, thus providing a ready and continuous supply of the molecules needed for further photosynthesis. This is a sort of complimentary, or short circuit, cycling which is very efficient indeed.

Green plants are the great *PRODUCERS*. Self-supporting *AUTOTROPHS*, they also provide food for all other living things. Especially valuable are those plants which concentrate large amounts of the minerals and nutrients needed for life. Plants can do this when they grow in optimum circumstances—often at the interface of land and water, where they have plenty of light, water, and a ready supply of nutrients and minerals—as in estuaries. Then they can spend all their time and energy growing and producing, not just fighting for survival.

Green plants are often considered in terms of their overall *PRODUCTIVITY*. They form the base of two food chains: the grazing animal food chain, and the food chain of the decomposers. These chains are linked together inseparably and cannot exist without one another. Together they form the web of life.

Enmeshed in the grid of green plants wrapped around the planet is a remarkable array of animals, including the insects. They have evolved in even greater variety and number than the plants, fitting themselves into every habitat and ecosystem to take advantage of a ready-made food supply. While the plants are the producers, the animals are the *CONSUMERS*, or *HETEROTROPHS*. The primary consumers make up the first link in the animal food chain, being *HERBIVORES*. These may be as small as larvae and as large as a deer. The secondary consumers are composed of the *CARNIVORES*, the meat eaters, the little fish that eat the larvae, the mountain lion that eats the deer—or once did. There are *OMNIVORES*, too, which eat anything they can get, plant or animal. There may be many links in this animal food chain, many levels of consumers, but at the top are always the *PREDATORS*, the egret, the shark, the man. With each exchange of food, some energy leaks out, radiating into space as heat, and so becoming lost to life on earth forever. Because of this, and because of the matter of size (it is hard to swallow something bigger than you are) there are fewer primary consumers than there are producers, and so on up the chain. It takes many diatoms to feed a hungry larvae and many larvae to feed the little fish. As food is passed along the food chain, nutrients, minerals, proteins—and poisons—are often concentrated and magnified. This is *BIOLOGICAL MAGNIFICATION*.

Consumers not only eat the plants, they also help to circulate and cycle the nutrients on which plant life depends. Indeed there is a constant give and take between plants and animals, even as there is between life itself and the earth.

It is, however, an inefficient system. Plants fix only a tiny fraction of the sun's energy—sometimes less than one per cent—and pass on only a fraction of what they fix, and much is lost in every trophic (or food) exchange. But, despite his technological ingenuity, man has found no way to improve on it.

In silent shadowy worlds, unseen and unremarked, the *DECOMPOSERS* live in numbers more abundant than any other form of life. They occupy the litter of forest floors, the soils of fields and meadows, the bottoms of lakes and tidal pools. They move with streams and oceans, they permeate the silts and muds and shallows of estuaries. Working tirelessly and endlessly, they unravel the fibres of dead leaves and unloose the particles of flowers and grass, of bones and flesh and sinew, unlocking essential nutrients and returning them to the pool of life. They play a most vital role in nature for, without them, the elements required for life would remain forever fastened away in the bodies of unliving things. We call them agents of decay, yet the decomposers are in fact the great recyclers and renewers of life.

137

Nature has designed them in various forms, but by far the greatest number are fungi and bacteria. Together they perform the initial breakdown of most organic material into *DETRITUS*. They are among the most extraordinary of living things, testament anew to life's inventiveness. They grow in myriad forms throughout the ecosphere, even in clouds.

The larger, showier fungi, the mushrooms of woods and meadows and marshes, spend most of their lives unseen, twining their threadlike webs, mycelia, inside of dead trees, through fields and salt marshes and in the debris of forest floors. In spring rains they push up their fruiting bodies, sometimes as bright as flags, and explode their spores to ride the winds as high as the stratosphere, floating to the very edge of outer space. Other fungi grow like fur in fuzzy molds, or join with algae to make the gray-green lichens that crust rocks, drape trees and coat the sod of some marshes.

The microscopic fungi occur in waters, soils, muds, silts and sands in prodigious numbers. Some are pathogenic, invading living diatoms and benthic algae, causing diseases in oysters and clams and certain fishes of the estuary and ocean. But most weave their webs inside of dead plant or animal life, prying apart the organic matter, even as they take energy from it.

Working with them in equally prodigious numbers—and so small that a billion could scarcely cloud a drop of water—are the bacteria. They float, drift, spin, wriggle and sail through water, or simply exist, fixed in mud, in air and water and soil. Shaped like rods, dots, crescents, filaments and spirals, they are among the toughest forms of life (and next to the viruses, probably the most primitive). Many live briefly and furiously, existing a scant ten minutes before they divide themselves into two new individuals. Multiplying by simple cell division, they can grow into enormous colonies in the span of a few hours. When conditions threaten them, many can form spores, infinitely tiny specks of dormant life, so tough they can endure great extremes of environmental change, waiting for years if need be for the right conditions to live again in their active form.

Some species of bacteria are, like certain of the fungi, pathogenic. But by far the greater number are friendly to all of life, including man, who, as noted earlier, requires certain of them to help digest his food, and who, without them, might have no food at all. With the fungi, the bacteria help to form the detritus which feeds countless numbers of plants and animals on which man in turn depends for his food.

Even as fungi are triggered by rain to send up their fruiting bodies, all living things have curious mechanisms which react to particular, important circumstances in their lives. Among the more interesting of these are the *BIOLOGICAL CLOCKS* which regulate our own human reactions, as well as those of one-celled plants and animals.

In this prodigious system that keeps life going on planet earth, it is clear that all living forms require each other, the land, the air and the water to survive. Earth works with and for life (if man will allow it). Earth's land forms play a vital role in supporting life, too. Each room in life's home supports much of the total structure. Without any room—without oceans, or shores, mountains, lakes, rivers, or estuaries—life could not continue as we know it.

CHAPTER 2:   Selected Bibliography
National Estuary Study: House Document No. 91-274, and Volumes II through VII. Washington, D.C.: Government Printing Office, 1970.
The National Estuarine Pollution Study: Senate Document 91-58. Washington, D.C.: Government Printing Office, 1970.

These government studies are both valuable. Chapter I of Senate Document 91-58 is a particularly helpful and comprehensive discussion of the estuary as a land form.

Lauff, George H. (ed.). *Estuaries:* AAAS Symposium. Washington, D.C.: American Association for the Advancement of Science, 1967.

The estuary's "bible," this is a very inclusive volume. Although some articles are highly technical, virtually every one bears reading. It is noteworthy, however, that throughout there is scarcely a mention of birds and the role of the estuary in their life-support system.

Teal, John and Mildred. *Life and Death of the Salt Marsh.* Boston, Mass.: Little, Brown and Company, 1969.

An excellent, readable account of east coast salt marshes.

Other Sources

Interviews with Gary Griggs, University of California, Santa Cruz; Joel F. Gustafson, California State University, San Francisco; Joel W. Hedgpeth, Oregon State University; James McCarty, Federal Water Quality Administration; James P. Heath, California State University, San Jose.

Specific References

Page 21: *National Estuarine Pollution Study,* page 5.
Page 21: J. L. McHugh in *Estuaries,* AAAS Symposium, page 581 and ff.
Page 22: K. O. Emery in *Estuaries,* AAAS Symposium, page 9.
Page 26: Michael Butler in *Science,* Vol. 176, No. 4039, page 1003.

CHAPTER 3:   Selected Bibliography
Alexopoulous, C. J. and H. C. Bold. *Algae and Fungi.* New York: The Macmillan Co., 1967.
Chapman, V. J. *Salt Marshes and Salt Deserts of the World.* New York: Interscience Publishers, Inc., 1962.

This is highly recommended, although the author still unaccountably subscribes to the idea that marshes should be "reclaimed"

Dawson, E. Yale. *Seashore Plants of Northern California.* Berkeley, Cal.: University of California Press, 1966. Paperback.
Doyle, William T. *Nonvascular Plants: Form and Function.* Belmont, Cal.: Wadsworth Publishing Co., 1965.
Hinde, H. P. *The Vertical Distribution of Salt Marsh Phanerogams in Relation to Tidal Levels.* Ecological Monographs: 24-2. 1954.
Howell, John Thomas. *Marin Flora.* Berkeley, Cal.: University of California Press, 1970.
Mason, Herbert L. *A Flora of the Marshes of California.* Berkeley, Cal.: University of California Press, 1957.
Molina, Al and Ann Rathbun. *The Zonation of the Conspicuous Phanerogams on Kent Island, Bolinas Lagoon.* Bolinas, Cal.: Bolinas Marine Station, College of Marin, 1968.

Odum, Eugene P. *The Role of Tidal Marshes in Estuarine Production.* New York State Conservation Dept., "Conservationist", June-July 1961.

Odum, Eugene P. *A Research Challenge: Evaluating the Productivity of Coastal and Estuarine Water.* Proceedings, 2nd Sea Grant Conf., University of Rhode Island, 1968.

Scagel, Robert F., et al. *An Evolutionary Survey of the Plant Kingdom.* Belmont, Cal.: Wadsworth Publishing Co., 1965. A classic.

Weier, T. Elliott, et al. *Botany, An Introduction To Plant Biology.* New York: John Wiley and Sons, Inc., 1970.

Other Sources
Interviews with Eugene P. Odum, University of Georgia; William Doyle, University of California, Santa Cruz; and John Thomas, Stanford University.

Specific References
Page 32: The classic studies referred to were conducted by Eugene P. Odum and his students and associates at the University of Georgia.

CHAPTER 4:   Selected Bibliography
Barnes, Robert D. *Invertebrate Zoology.* Philadelphia: W. B. Saunders Co., 1968.

Blair, Albert J., Jr. *Guide to the Plankton of Bolinas Lagoon.* Occasional Paper. College of Marin, Kentfield, Cal., 1969.

Hedgpeth, Joel W. (ed.). *Treatise on Marine Ecology and Paleoecology.* Vols. I and II. Geological Society of America, 1963.

Ibid. *Introduction to Seashore Life.* Berkeley, Cal.: University of California Press, 1967. Paperback.

Hedgpeth's work is uniformly well written, researched, and worth reading.

MacGinitie, G. E. and MacGinitie, N. *Natural History of Marine Animals.* New York: McGraw-Hill Book Co., Inc., 1949.

Although written more than two decades ago, this remains one of the best and most entertaining books on the natural history of marine animals.

Ricketts, Edward F. and Jack Calvin. (Rev. and ed. by Joel W. Hedgpeth.) *Between Pacific Tides.* Stanford, Cal.: Stanford University Press, 1969.

A classic. Written in 1939, it now has the unmistakable flavor of Hedgpeth's wit in addition to the fine earlier work of Ricketts and Calvin. Required reading for any student of west coast seashore life.

Other Sources
Interviews with Donald P. Abbott, Stanford University; James Carlton, California Academy of Science; Cedric Davern and Todd Newberry, University of California, Santa Cruz; Starker Leopold, University of California, Berkeley; Gordon Chan and Craig Hanson, College of Marin.

CHAPTER 5:   Selected Bibliography
Bent, Arthur Cleveland. *Life Histories of North American Gulls and Terns.* Washington, D.C.: U.S. Government Printing Office, 1921.

Check-list of North American Birds. Fifth Edition. American Ornithologists' Union. Baltimore, Md.: Lord Baltimore Press, Inc.

Dawson, Leon William: *The Birds of California,* Vol. II. San Diego, Cal.:

South Moulton Co., 1923.

Dorst, Jean: *The Migrations of Birds.* Boston, Mass.: Houghton Mifflin Co., 1962.

Kortright, Francis H. *The Ducks, Geese and Swans of North America.* Washington, D.C.: American Wildlife Institute, 1942.

Written for hunters, and too big for a pocket or knapsack, this is the outstanding guidebook for North American wild fowl.

Matthiessen, Peter. *The Shorebirds of North America.* New York: Viking Press, 1967.

Parmellee, David F. *Breeding Behaviours of the Sanderling in the Canadian High Arctic.* The Living Bird. 9th Annual. Buffalo, N.Y. December, 1970.

Peterson, Roger Tory. *A Field Guide to Western Birds.* Cambridge, Mass.: The Riverside Press, 1961. Paperback.

The standard guide for birdwatchers.

Point Reyes Bird Observatory: *Check-list of Birds of Bolinas Lagoon.* Bolinas, 1971.

Rand, Austin L. *Ornithology, an Introduction.* New York: Signet, 1967. Paperback.

Robbins, Chandler S. et al. *Birds of North America.* New York: Golden Press, 1966. Paperback.

It's a toss-up between this and the Peterson Guide for the serious bird-watcher. This volume has excellent maps, giving ranges, as well as color pictures which are a great help.

Welty, Joel Carl: *The Life of Birds.* Philadelphia: W. B. Saunders Co., 1962.

Other Sources

Interviews with Frank Pitelka, University of California, Berkeley; David de Sante, Stanford University, and Clerin Zumwalt, Audubon Canyon Ranch, Bolinas.

Specific References

Page 76. Quoted by Gardner Strout in *Shorebirds of North America*, page 12. *Note:* There are two schools of thought on capitalizing species names when using English rather than Latin. I have chosen the more informal, employing the lower-case throughout.

CHAPTER 6:   ### Selected Bibliography

Barghoorn, Elso S. *The Oldest Fossils.* Scientific American, Vol. 224, no. 5. pp 30-49. May, 1971.

Commoner, Barry. *The Closing Circle.* New York: Alfred A. Knopf, 1971.

Dolhinow, Phyllis and Vincent Sarich (eds.). *Background for Man.* Boston, Mass.: Little, Brown and Co., 1971.

Haynes, Robert H. and Phillip C. Hanawalt (eds.). *The Molecular Basis of Life.* San Francisco, Cal.: W. H. Freeman Co., 1968.

Laughlin, W. S. and R. H. Osborne, Introduction. *Human Variation and Origins.* San Francisco, Cal.: W. H. Freeman Co., 1967.

Ponnamperuma, Cyril. *Chemical Evolution and the Origin of Life.* New York State Journal Of Medicine. Vol. 70, #10. May 15, 1970.

Ibid and Norman W. Gabel. *Current Status of Chemical Studies on the Origin of Life.* Space Life Sciences 1, 64-96. D. Reidel, Dorsrecht-Holland, 1968.

Romer, Alfred S. *The Vertebrate Story.* Chicago, Ill.: University of Chicago Press, 1959.

Thompson, D'Arcy. Abr. and ed. by John Tyler Bonner. *On Growth and Form.* Cambridge University Press, 1961.

A highly provocative book, although heavy reading in places.

Other Sources

Interviews with Elso S. Barghoorn of Harvard University, and Cyril Ponnamperuma, Delbert Philpott and Robert Debs of NASA.

Specific References

Pages 86: Barry Commoner in *The Closing Circle,* pages 20 and 299.

Page 86: Elso S. Barghoorn in *The Oldest Fossils,* page 34.

Page 87: Donald P. Abbott, personal communication.

Page 87: Gordon Gunter in *Treatise on Marine Ecology and Paleoecology* (see Bibliography, Chapter 4): Vol. 1, page 145.

Page 88: Joel W. Hedgpeth in *Treatise on Marine Ecology and Paleoecology:* Vol. 1, page 696.

CHAPTER 7:   Selected Bibliography

Bresler, Jack R. (ed). *Environments of Man.* Reading, Mass.: Addison Wesley Co., 1968.

Clark, Grahame. *World Prehistory.* Cambridge University Press, 1961.

Clark, J. Desmond. *The Prehistory of Africa.* New York: Praeger Publishing Co., 1970.

Griffin, James B. (ed.). *Archeology of the Eastern United States.* Chicago, Ill.: University of Chicago Press, 1952.

Hardy, Sir Alister. *Was Man More Aquatic in the Past?* The New Scientist. Vol. 7., 1960.

Johnson, Frederick, et al. *The Boylston Street Fishweir.* Andover, Mass.: Robert S. Peabody Foundation Scientific Papers. Vols. II and IV, 1942 and 1949.

This is an elegant anthropological detective story.

Pilbeam, David. *The Ascent of Man.* New York: Macmillan Co., 1972. Paperback.

An excellent discussion of man's evolution.

Willey, Gordon R. *An Introduction to American Archeology,* Vol. I. Englewood Cliffs, N.J.: Prentice-Hall Inc., 1966.

Other Sources

Interviews with Phillip F. C. Greear of Shorter College, Georgia; Roger Heglar, and Mike Moratto of California State University at San Francisco.

Specific References

Page 93: *Environments of Man,* pages 169-176.

Page 100: Joel W. Hedgpeth, personal communication.

CHAPTER 8:   Selected Bibliography

An Environmental Management Program for Bolinas Lagoon, California. Washington, D.C.: The Conservation Foundation, 1971.

The Natural Resources of Bolinas Lagoon. Sacramento, Calif.: State of California, Department of Fish and Game, 1970.

This is the best discussion of Bolinas Lagoon, and its status.

Gustafson, Joel F. *Ecological Studies, Bolinas Lagoon.* Reports 1, 2 and 3. Prepared for County of Marin et al. 1969.

Kelly, Isabel. *Kelly's Manuscripts,* Vols. I and II. University of California, Berkeley. Lowie Museum of Anthropology. 1969. Unpublished.

Geologic Guidebook of the San Francisco Bay Counties. Bulletin 154. California Department of Natural Resources, Division of Mines. Ferry Building, San Francisco, 1951.

   Full of local information and color, and a remarkable buy.

Munro-Fraser, J. P. *History of Marin County.* San Francisco, Cal.: Alley-Bowen & Co., 1880.

Mason, Jack. *Point Reyes.* Point Reyes Station, Cal.: DeWolfe Printing, 1970.

Shapley, Harlow. *Beyond the Observatory.* New York: Charles Scribner's Sons, 1967.

Other Sources

Interviews with Thomas Barfield, Sherman Smith, and Greg Hewlett of Bolinas. The wealth of notes and memorabilia Mrs. James Jenkins provided was invaluable in assembling the history of Bolinas.

Specific References

Page 113: References to the "1880 history" on this and following pages are from Munro-Fraser, J. P. *History of Marin:* chapter on Bolinas.

Page 114: Oscar L. Shafter in a letter to his father, February 17, 1857.

Page 115: Stephen Richardson, son of William A. Richardson of Sausalito.

NOTES ON ECOLOGY: Selected Bibliography

Bates, Marsden. *The Forest and the Sea.* New York: The New American Library, 1960.

Buchsbaum, Ralph. *Basic Ecology.* Pittsburgh, Pa.: Boxwood Press, 1967.

Odum, Eugene P. *Ecology.* Modern Biology Series. New York: Holt, Rinehart and Winston, 1963.

Storer, John H. *The Web of Life.* New York: The New American Library, 1953.

   These four paperbacks comprise a very brief, readable introduction to the complex subject of ecology. Also recommended are the books of Aldo Leopold, Loren Eiseley, Henry David Thoreau, Rachel Carson and John Muir. All are sensitive, personal interpretations of the subject.

Specific References

Page 130: Garrett Hardin in *California Medicine,* Vol. 113, page 41. November, 1970. ●

Acknowledgments

This book came about because the College of Marin offered a marine biology course at Bolinas Lagoon; because Al Molina, who gave the course, is a gifted and inspiring teacher; and because I took the course in 1969. I am grateful for this combination of circumstances. It opened my eyes to the extraordinary world of the estuary and to the fact that so little interpretive writing had been published about it.

An interpretive work this book is meant to be. It does not pretend to be a scientific treatise. I have tried, however, to keep it accurate. I am grateful to the scientists and experts who were unfailingly kind and generous in sharing their knowledge with me. Their names appear in the section on sources. In particular, I thank H. Thomas Harvey of the California State University, San Jose, and Al Molina of the College of Marin, both of whom read my text and made invaluable suggestions. My thanks go, too, to Rodger Heglar of the California State University, San Francisco, who read Part Two; to John Thomas of Stanford University, who read Chapter 3; and to John Smail and Gary Page of the Point Reyes Bird Observatory, who gave me helpful criticism on Chapter 5. These people are, of course, not responsible for the content of the book nor for any errors I may have made.

Early in the preparation of the book, I had a hard choice to make. I could either give a few aspects of the estuary in-depth consideration, or I could provide a general look at the bigger picture. I chose the latter approach, believing it important to gain a broad perspective of this interesting land form. I am mindful that this choice has resulted in the omission of many fascinating—and important—details, and this I regret.

I am keenly aware that there are different concepts and definitions of what an estuary is. Perhaps some people will question my considering Bolinas Lagoon as an estuary. I have done so, using for my authority numerous references including the work of Clyde Wahrhaftig of the University of California at Berkeley. Wahrhaftig describes Bolinas Lagoon as "a triangular estuary" in the Conservation Foundation report. (See Selected Bibliography, Chapter 8 References.)

No book is the work of a single person alone. Along with those mentioned above, a number of people helped make this book possible. My editor, John Mitchell, provided understanding and encouragement during trying times. Paul Brooks read the manuscript and gave me expert advice. Vivian Breckenfeld lent me her home and her blessing. Ada Schwartz cheerfully typed and re-typed many sections of the book. Mrs. James Jenkins of San Francisco provided her personal historical notes as well as her home in Bolinas, where most of the book was written. And Miss Madeline Moses of Weston, Conn., gave both encouragement and support. I thank them all. Most of all, I thank my close family, including Mary Ruth Watson, who put up with me during the nearly three years it took to write this book.

Peggy Wayburn
San Francisco
August 1972